Knaust.
The complete guide to Aïda

The complete guide to AÏDA

Written by
Rebecca Knaust
Illustrated by
Maurice Hughes

Concept and Art Direction by
Don McAfee

McAfee Books
a division of McAfee Music Corporation
New York

A McAfee Book for Lorenz Press

ISBN No. 0-89328-024-0

Contents

Foreword

It is done. Sealed in an airless crypt, his beloved Aida dying in his arms, Radames, just short days before hailed as a savior, favorite of the gods, struggles to accept the fate his own honor and loyal heart have decreed. The stern justice was swift, irrevocable. Once a proud warrior, granted even the prized hand of the Pharoh's own daughter for delivering their people from the despised Ethiopian aggressors, he had earned, in a single unguarded moment, the miserable sentence befitting a traitor: his death must be cruel. There are no cheering crowds here, no feasting victors, no whirling dancers. They are gone, bittersweet memories, as silent as the trumpets that proclaimed his triumph throughout all Egypt.

It grows darker. He begins to surrender, slowly, hearing nothing save muffled chants from above, the prayers for his soul.

And we are left wondering, uncertain. Was he himself those last, oddly almost giddy moments? Can it honestly comfort him to know that at last he and Aida, his treasure, his inspiration, are united in death as they could not be in life? We will really never know.

That Giuseppe Verdi's *Aida* was destined to become perhaps the most popular opera ever written was apparent even as the curtain fell on this, the final scene, at the 1871 Christmas Eve Cairo opening. An exotic audience in an exotic land thrilled to its breathtaking spectacle and suffered the anguish of a young slave and her lover as their dreams of happiness crumble about them. Set in ancient Egypt, a long vanished but not forgotten kingdom which continues to intrigue, *Aida* magically captures all the rich colors and forbidden mysteries our imaginations can conjure of that far away time and place.

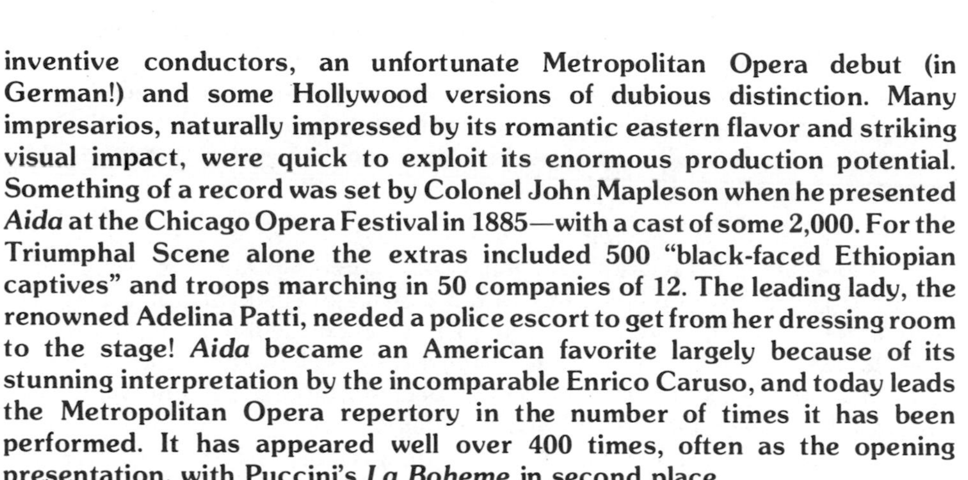

inventive conductors, an unfortunate Metropolitan Opera debut (in German!) and some Hollywood versions of dubious distinction. Many impresarios, naturally impressed by its romantic eastern flavor and striking visual impact, were quick to exploit its enormous production potential. Something of a record was set by Colonel John Mapleson when he presented *Aida* at the Chicago Opera Festival in 1885—with a cast of some 2,000. For the Triumphal Scene alone the extras included 500 "black-faced Ethiopian captives" and troops marching in 50 companies of 12. The leading lady, the renowned Adelina Patti, needed a police escort to get from her dressing room to the stage! *Aida* became an American favorite largely because of its stunning interpretation by the incomparable Enrico Caruso, and today leads the Metropolitan Opera repertory in the number of times it has been performed. It has appeared well over 400 times, often as the opening presentation, with Puccini's *La Boheme* in second place.

Of course *Aida*, as any other opera, must be heard and hummed and tapped out on table tops in order to be fully savored. Thus this volume presents the highlights and especially successful passages of the work,with original Italian verse; each selection is accompanied by a discussion of the progress of the music and the story-line at that point. One need not be a wizard at the piano or the possessor of remarkable vocal cords to enjoy this unique opportunity to explore a much loved masterpiece. Provide a bit of imagination, and it will surely cast its enchanting spell.

In the end all, save the gods, must lose. The vaguely sinister priests, always in the background offering advice and warning, sentence, try and comdemn Radames with murderous efficiency. Amonasro is killed. Amneris, for all her power, is unable to control her feelings long enough to redeem the warrior she knows will never love her. And Aida, accepting the doom of her lover, ends her life with his.

If the resounding success *Aida* enjoyed at Cairo was something of a social, not a musical triumph, its subsequent openings at Milan and London, assured its creator that it was not merely Cairo's lavish furnishings, elaborate sets and stunning costumes which impressed even the more hostile critics of the day. A grand opera, written in the traditional Italian idiom, *Aida* was carefuly conceived. Its success was no accident. Painstakingly styled detail by detail, it is well placed and markedly enhanced by no-nonsense vigor, a characteristic of the composer. No time is lost setting up the drama of the plot or identifying the characters. All the essentials are explained by the conclusion of the first act. That the unforgettable theatrical trappings, its ballets, huge choruses, scores of captives, marching troops and fan-bearers, even a brass band on stage, all of which more than incidentally lend the opera its uncanny air of authenticity, are handled so that they enhance, not detract from, the story is a fair measure of Verdi's well seasoned skill in a demanding and complex form.

Throughout its distinguished career, *Aida*, christened "the best opera created in Italy", has retained its wide popularity, managing to survive the assaults of changing tastes, indifferent or ill-suited performers, overly

The opera tells a simple story, and if the characters are not nearly as compelling and dramatic as is their situation, they are appealingly human. An unexpected war challenges the strength and conviction of each. Patriotism, loyalty and honor clash again and again. *Aida* interprets man's more primitive emotions—love, pride, jealousy, revenge—and carries them quickly, with a master's certainty, towards their ultimate, inevitable, conclusion.

Aida, a slave of the Egyptian Pharoh's tempermental daughter, Amneris, is in truth an Ethiopian princess, daughter of King Amonasro. Somehow her captors are unaware of her royal lineage. She has won the love of Radames, a captain in the Egyptian army. But Aida's rival in this love is none other than her mistress, and while Radames longs only for the unfortunate captive, the indulged and intolerant Amneris means to secure his affections for herself.

As the story unfolds, Radames easily satisfies his military ambitions by leading the defeat of the invading Ethiopians under the command of Aida's father, Amonasro. Amonasro is taken prisoner but his identity too is at first unguessed by the Egyptians. Poor Aida, proud of her lover's victory but torn by the capture of Amonasro and the humiliation of her people, suffers unceasingly. Tortured by her own conscience and the suspicious taunts and undisguised anger of Amneris, who is all to eager to claim her reluctant groom, she sees her hopes shattered. Even her father spurns her when she cannot bring herself to betray Radames as Amonasro, hoping to re-engage the Egyptians in combat, suggests—however worthy the cause. But alas, Radames, in an ill-timed moment of weakness, betrays himself, and soon finds he is to as enthusiastically damned as a traitor both to his country and royal intended as he was once championed as a hero.

Biographical Background

"... copying reality can be a good thing; but the invention of reality is better, much better".

G. Verdi

Camille du Locle was an ambitious man. Surely if he could persuade the great Verdi to write the opera proposed to celebrate the opening of Egypt's Suez Canal he would be that much closer to the directorship of the Paris Opera-Comique he sought. But how? Verdi, apparently not especially anxious to work so soon after the dishearteningly modest success of *Don Carlos* and the failure of a revised *Macbeth*, had twice refused to consider any of his ideas.

During the winter of 1869-70, du Locle made a journey up the Nile with Auguste Ferdinand F. Mariette, a French Egyptologist who had been awarded the honorary titles of "Bey" and "Pasha" for his work. Inspired by local legends and some curious archeological findings, Mariette Bey had written and published in limited edition a romantic little story. He had even proposed that the Khedive of Egypt commission an original opera based on the story to comemmorate the Canal's opening. The Khedive, Ishmael Pasha, had been educated on the continent and enjoyed European culture, particularly its music, and so thought such an opera a marvelous idea. Cairo's newly completed opera house would be a fine showcase for its special presentation. It was decided, diplomatically enough, to approach "one of the best composers" for the job: Germany's Wagner, France's Gounod or Italy's Verdi. It was du Locle who had insisted only Verdi would do. But he was running out of time.

Trying again early in 1870, du Locle, who had worked with Verdi as co-librettist on *Don Carlos*, but Mariette Bey's story in brief scenario form and submitted this "Egyptian sketch" to the often difficult composer for his consideration. This time du Locle's persistence paid off. Verdi, delighted with it at once, agreed to write the score.

When the business details were settled, it had been agreed that Verdi was to pay for the libretto, while the Khedive would deposit the considerable sum of 150,000 gold francs in the Rothschild Bank in Paris—Verdi's fee for the score. The opera was to be ready by December, 1870, for the premier in Cairo in January, 1871, after which the world rights would belong to Verdi.

At late as June of 1870 no Italian text had yet been written, but Verdi, unconcerned, had already given this opera a good deal of thought. It was, of course, to be a thoroughly Italian opera despite the Egyptian opening, and he had no intention of making any reference to Suez, which had, in fact, already been in operation since November of 1869.

Verdi then asked Antonio Ghislanzoni of Lecco to write the libretto in Italian. Ghislanzoni, delighted with the offer, did not even bother to ask what his fee for the work would be. His eccentric background included one career as an operatic baritone which ended when his voice failed him in 1854, and another, that of writer. He had previously worked with Verdi on the revision of *La Forzo del Destino*, and eventually produced some eighty librettos, as well as plays, poetry and novels; he also edited Ricordi's*Gazzetta Musicale*. And more than incidentally, that great music publishing house, for many years associated with Verdi as his publisher, could not have been more pleased that he was working again. They knew they stood to make a great deal of money on *Aida*—and they did.

His initial reluctance to work on an opera forgotten, Verdi fussed over *Aida* like an old spinster aunt inspecting her teacups for chips. A word here, an entire scene there, this line, that meter... what about the bass drums and kettledrums? is the pitch (864 vibrations) correct? no, no, the cabaletta is too long... the action must be clearer... the opening must "smell of Egypt". By the time he had rewritten his patient librettist's verse for the last time, no one doubted him when he declared, "I repeat now for the twentieth time that the only thing I am looking for is success".

The work progressed very rapidly, despite his constant revisions, at something like one act per month. Finished by the middle of November, 1870, it was ready, as agreed, for the December delivery.

No one, however, had counted on the outbreak of the Franco-Prussian War in July, 1870, or the seige of Paris that followed. Verdi was greatly disturbed by the war and buried himself in the *Aida* project to avoid depressing himself by thinking about it. But as the war dragged on, final negotiations with Mariette Bey could not proceed as the scholar was trapped in Paris, along with all of *Aida's* costumes and scenery which had been assembled there, during the seige of that city; few were willing to rely on any communications with a city reduced to depending on balloons and pigeons for news with any certainty.

All this presented quite a few problems for the Egyptians. In the original contract Verdi had stipulated that *Aida* was to be produced at La Scala soon after the Cairo performance, and there was some real concern on their part that Verdi would take advantage of the war to go ahead in Milan without waiting for Cairo. Paris finally surrendered in January, 1871, but by that time it was too late to produce the opera at the current season in Cairo. Verdi, however, assured them that he could hardly not accept the war as a legitimate cause for delay. He had, in fact, already suspended negotiations with Milan.

The Cairo premier was re-scheduled for December, 1871. The first Milan presentation, scheduled six weeks later, was to have its own production, cast and conductor. Verdi himself was preparing for La Scala. He had no intention of going to Cairo, and never did have, not even to attend opening night. But he had agreed to assist in those arrangements he could. During that year there were all the usual discussions as to singers and conductors, and Verdi had

some definite suggestions. In earlier days, Verdi would have personally conducted the first three performances before turning the task over to a well-rehearsed successor, but orchestras had become larger and more complex by 1871, and the direction of a competent specialist was indispensible.

Verdi's first choice to conduct was the gifted Angelo Mariani. The two had once been the closest of friends, and Verdi continued to admire Mariani as a musician, but their friendship had ended not long before, quite unhappily, under somewhat complicated circumstances not completely understood.

For years Mariani had been the lover of Bohemian-born soprano Teresa Stolz. That too had recently ended. There were many reasons for this break, but according to the sensationalist press of the day, Stolz had left Mariani for the affections of another great musician—Verdi, of course. It is true that Stolz and Verdi saw a good deal of one another—professionally. And she was to sing the title role of *Aida* at the La Scala premier so they were necessarily in frequent touch with one another. Described as tall and staturesque, she was uniquely gifted with "presence", a quality a performer either does or does not have the good luck to possess. There can be no denying that she commanded Verdi's admiring attention. Even his friends admitted that he was much taken with her. We know he liked her voice. He added the supremely difficult and very beautiful "o cieli azzuri" introduction to the "O patria mia" passage with Stolz in mind (it has remained in the score ever since). She was always his favorite *Aida*, even signing some of her letters to him with that name. But what else, if anything, may have impressed him about her we are likely never to know for certain. At any rate, Mariani proved unavailable as conductor.

Since Mariani could not be secured for either production, Franco Faccio was eventually settled on to conduct at Milan, and he did well under Verdi's watchful supervision. Giovanni Bottesini, about whom little is known, conducted at Cairo, and by all accounts appears to have been more than adequate. Verdi was in correspondence with Bottesini before the Cairo opening and sent him an amended version of the stretto at the end of the duet between Amneris and Aida in the second act. Indeed, Verdi kept making revisions right up until opening night at Milan. He wrote again to Bottesini for a report about the final duet. He was particularly anxious to know if it worked as he hoped it would, explaining that though he had rewritten it any number of times, "in view of the fact that it belongs to what I may call the vaporous style, maybe the effect will not correspond to my intentions".

This concern for the details of the opera continued long after the Maestro took his thirty-two curtain calls at La Scala. He was exceptionally pleased with the success of *Aida*, and justly proud of its quality. He was also very protective of the integrity of its last polished version by his own hand. When he later heard that conductors were taking various liberties with the score, that singers were transposing arias up and down and similarly tampering with the original, he angrily threatened to have *Aida* withdrawn rather than permit it to be subjected to such offensive practices.

Aida's triumph made Verdi very, very well known, almost public property. And he did not like it one bit. Perhaps he was the Grand Old Man of Italian Opera, but he stubbornly clung to his peasant origins throughout his eighty-eight years. Indeed, he worried about his gardens and horses nearly as much as his music. It was his great delight to retreat with his second wife, Giuseppina Strepponi, to the Villa Sant' Agata, near Busseto, which he purchased along with its neighboring farm land in 1848. There he could escape all the gossip and the prying, the critics and the intrigues—all the attendant nuisances of his profession—and plant trees.

Strepponi, a former soprano, was a woman of great humor, discretion and personal charm. Theirs was an almost ideal relationship, though, for reasons Verdi consistently refused to explain, they lived togther for some ten years before deciding to marry in 1859. This unconventional courtship aside, she remained his devoted and loving companion until her death in November of 1897, always on hand to calm his ready temper, soften his not infrequent arrogant gruffness, and guard his treasured privacy.

Born October 10, 1813 of simple parents in the Duchy of Parma's tiny Le Roncole, Giuseppe Verdi's keen interest in all things musical surfaced early. The village organist, whom the young boy quickly surpased, gave him his first music lessons. By a stroke of extra-ordinary good luck, the boy's talents came to the attention of Antonio Barezzi, a well-to-do merchant and music lover from nearly Busseto, and under his patronage Verdi's training continued. Barezzi blessed Verdi with the generosity, faith and support without which he might well have ended up a grocer and wine seller like his father.

He began to study under Busseto's choirmaster-organist. As he progressed he gave piano lessons and started composing. Though he never forgot his disappointment when at eighteen he was rejected for admission by the famed Milan Music Conservatory, he was nevertheless determined to continue with his music. He next became a student of Vincenzo Lavigna, a minor opera official and Conservatory teacher. Lavigna gave Verdi lessons in the classic harmony and counterpoint of the early masters he never forgot.

His studies with Lavigna completed, Verdi's student years were behind him. His career then took several directions. After some political difficulties he became Official Master of Music to the Commune of Busseto. He began to conduct at Milan's Philodramatic Theater and was asked to write a cantata and an opera for that stage. In 1836 Verdi married Barezzi's daughter Margherita, and began to compose his first opera. Though he was later to write his best known works in three to four months, this first required two to three years to complete. Financially still dependent on his kindly patron, these were years of personal tragedy and profesional disappointment for the young composer. By the time he was twenty-six, death had claimed first a daughter and son, then his wife. Short weeks after this final loss the Malicious gossip of Milan's opera fans following the utter failure of a comic opera he had written drove him to vow never to compose again.

No one paid any attention to this of course. Opera was big business in 19th Century Italy—one failure did not break a career. The loyal Barezzi, Giovanni Ricordi of Italy's famed music publishing house and others already interested in Verdi as a composer, including La Scala's impresario Bartolomeo Merelli, patiently stood by him, waiting for the succes they knew would come. It was not a long wait. An 1842 production of his *Nabucco* brought him easy popularity. It was only the beginning.

The operas composed during this early period (1839-49) are the most numerous. It was not until his second period (1850-67) that he achieved musical maturity and world-wide recognition, composing such favorites as *Rigoletto* and *Il Trovatore*. *Aida* (1871) is generally recognized as a bridge between the second and final periods, when he was accorded the critical acclaim that matched his enormous popularity with *Otello* (1887) and *Falstaff* (1893).

Italian opera reached its second 19th century peak with the works of Verdi. For his immediate forerunners, Cioacchino Rossina (1792-1868), Vincenzo Bellini (1801-1835) and Gaetano Donizetti (1797-1848), he always maintained, at least publically, the greatest possible respect. By chance all three were swept aside as competitors just as Verdi began his work in earnest, leaving him virtually alone to command the Italian operatic arena. For his own contemporaries he had far less tolerance.

He never had much interest in French composers, considering their creative powers to be quite limited. He once wrote, "they make and remake; they seek but never find", rather neatly summing up his estimation of their abilities. Of Charles F. Gounod (1818-1893), once considered for the *Aida* project, he had this criticism, quite interesting in light of the opera's strong points: "Gounod is a very great musician, the first master of France, but he had no dramatic fibre... the word is nearly always expressed, but not the situation. His characters are not skilfully drawn, and his drama is lacking in atmosphere". For Louis H. Berlioz (1803-1869) he had mixed feelings, ultimately negative. In the work of Alexandre C.L. (called Georges) Bizet (1838-1875) he found all the contrasts he thought necessary in good opera, but felt it suffered by its lack of idealism. The music of Jules E.F. Massenet (1842-1912) he simply disliked—intensely.

German composers, most particularly Richard Wagner (1813-1883), presented quite another problem for Verdi. They were not so easily dismissed. Wagner was the first foreigner to seriously challenge the supremacy of the Italians in a field they had always considered to be exclusively their own. His achievements were widely discussed in the newspapers of the day. Verdi became quite panicky about the whole thing. This panic became a fierce bitterness in the 1870's. "A fine result after thirty-five years to be called an imitator!" was his reply when much of the brilliance of *Aida* was attributed, quite incorrectly, to the direct influence of Wagner.

Verdi and Wagner, born the same year, matured artistically about the same time and both were in competition for critical and popular followings in relatively close quarters. It was natural to compare the two. But there was a major difference in their work often overlooked at the time. Verdi always wrote principally for the voice, while Wagner used the voice as part of the orchestra. In *Aida* all the great climaxes are expressed vocally. The same is not true in the important works of Wagner. It is true that Verdi's later works show a much great concern for the orchestra than had previously been shown in Italian opera—very much to its benefit. But if German influence was responsible for the increased refinement of Italian orchestration, the necessary balance between the vocal and orchestral elements that Verdi achieved in his final works, then it is a bit puzzling that he should react with such fury to the suggestion that Wagner may have been his inspiration. It should be remembered, however, that though he had doubtless heard of the works of Wagner in the past, he had completed the score of *Aida* before seeing *Logengrin*, his first Wagner opera, in Bologna in 1871.

Wagner remained Verdi's most dangerous rival, but he was ultimately the one contemporary composer Verdi most admired. Verdi undeniably disliked what he first encountered of Wagner's music, calling the *Tannhauser* Overture "crazy" on hearing it at a concert in Paris in 1865, but with time he found much to admire about Wagner's music. He also admired Wagner's greatest contemporary, Giacomo Meyerbeer (1791-1864) for his musicianship and theatrical gifts, but was not unaware of Meyerbeer's serious shortcomings. Indeed, Verdi's handling of theatrical dramatic procedure shows much more the influence of Meyerbeer than of any of his other contemporaries.

In later years, apart from Verdi, there were only two really exceptional composers working in Italy, Giacomo Puccini (1858-1924) and Alfredo Catalani's (1854-1893). Unfortunately, Verdi was basically unimpresed by either. He paid scant attention to Puccini's work and convinced himself, somehow, that Catalani, who was to die tragically young, was out to ruin the very character of Italian opera. He seemed to have more admiration for the work of Pietro Mascagni (1863-1945), then mistakenly named by the Italian press as Verdi's successor, whose work, though often crude and vulgar, does have considerable more in common with his own than that of either Catalani or Puccini.

Verdi instinctively knew something was wrong with Italian opera, sensed that the future was growing less and less bright, but he had trouble recognizing the real problem. Always a staunch supporter of his own definition of patriotism, he decided at first to blame foreign influences for the increasingly sorry state of the Italian operatic tradition. It must be "Germanism", he thought, that was threatening to ruin the character of Italy's opera. Young composers were submitting to foreign ideas and trading away their birthright, to glorify the human voice, and instead thinking of nothing but the orchestra. But it was not that simple.

In fact, his fear of the Germans and Wagner was really groundless. Wagner never did pose a real threat to Italian music. His influence, though considerable in France and England, was relatively minor in Ialy. The real problem was that Italian operatic genius was withering on its own vine. And in his later years, before his death by a stroke on January 27, 1901, Verdi sadly saw much of the truth.

"Good operas have been rare at all times" he observed, "now they have become virtually impossible. Why? Because too much music is being written; because there is too much striving after effect, because obscurity, not light, has become the aim of the artist. Because we are striving to create the grandiose and the inflated—not the great, and from the grandiose emerges the petty and the baroque".

It is significant that for all the activity of the 1890's, Italian operatic genius, having reached its heights with Verdi's *Otello* and *Falstaff*, died out, for all intents and purposes, with the death of Puccini just a quarter of a century later.

Verdi as a young man.

The Bettmann Archive

Verdi conducting the orchestra in the first performance of Aida.

The Bettmann Archive

Charcoal drawing of Verdi by Shizzo del Baldini

The Bettmann Archive

A portrait of Verdi by Giovanni Boldoni.
The Bettmann Archive

Siuseppina Strepponi at the piano.
The Bettmann Archive

AÏDA

Grand Opera in Four Acts
Music by Giuseppe Verdi
Libretto by Antonio Ghislanzoni
Original Language: Italian

AIDA: Major characters and their relationship to one another:

Aida, daughter of Amonasro, King of Ethiopia, and slave of Amneris, princess of Egypt. In love with Radames ....Soprano

Radames, captain of the Egyptian army and Aida's lover ....Tenor

Amneris, daughter of the King of Egypt, and mistress of Aida. She is also in love with Radames ....Mezzo-soprano

Amonasro, father of Aida and King of Ethiopia ....Baritone

Ramphis, High Priest of Egypt ....Bass

King of Egypt, father of Amneris ....Bass

An Egyptian Messenger ....Tenor

High Priestess of Egypt ....Soprano

Priests and priestesses; soldiers; royal attendants; heralds; slaves; Ethiopian captives; slaves to Amneris; Egyptian citizens, etc.

The Opera

Prelude

As if to somehow belie the stirring drama and wrenching emotional conflicts *Aida* is so soon to reveal, the opera opens, unexpectedly, with an orchestral prelude ingeniously wrought of two themes associated with action. The sobering and ominous motif identifying the Egyptian priests, later heard in Act II's Triumphal Scene and in the Judgment Scene of Act IV, is combined with "Aida's Theme", which will be repeated at her entrance in the first scenes in Acts I and II and again in Act III. So combined, the two themes evolve as still another musical entity, lyrical, restrained, and yet anticipatory, wholly effective. A more traditional overture, which Verdi did take the trouble to write, if only to reject it, could serve as no better, more evocative, an introduction.

The score throughout is remarkable for its abundance of melodic invention, descriptive contrast and lush harmonic and orchestral coloring. For the first time, Verdi's dance music is fluent and meaningful. His use of woodwinds is particularly expressive, and he had considerable success handling the difficult but especially stageworthy open-noted long trumpets put to imaginative use in the memorable march sequence. The "eastern" tonal effects are achieved through adroit instrumentation and harmonization and unusual melodic intervals. Even when poetic, the music never sacrifices its drama.

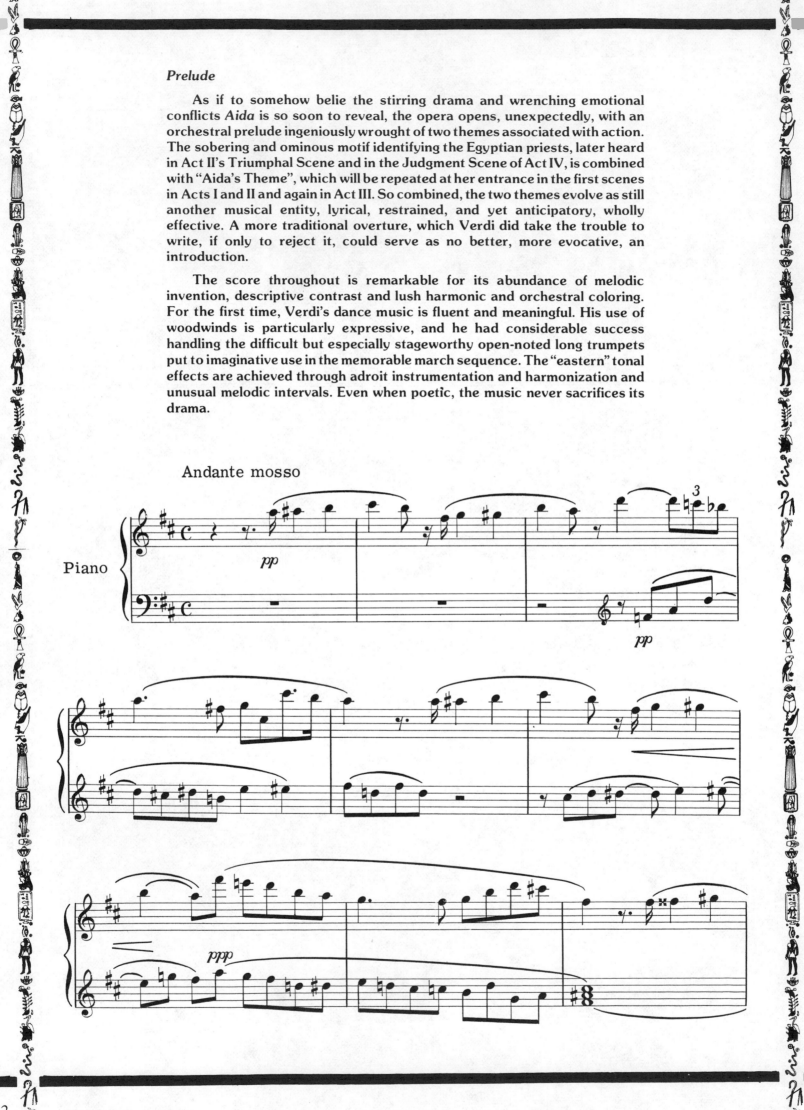

pp
cresc.
p
ppp
ppp
r.h.

pp
cresc.
ff
ff

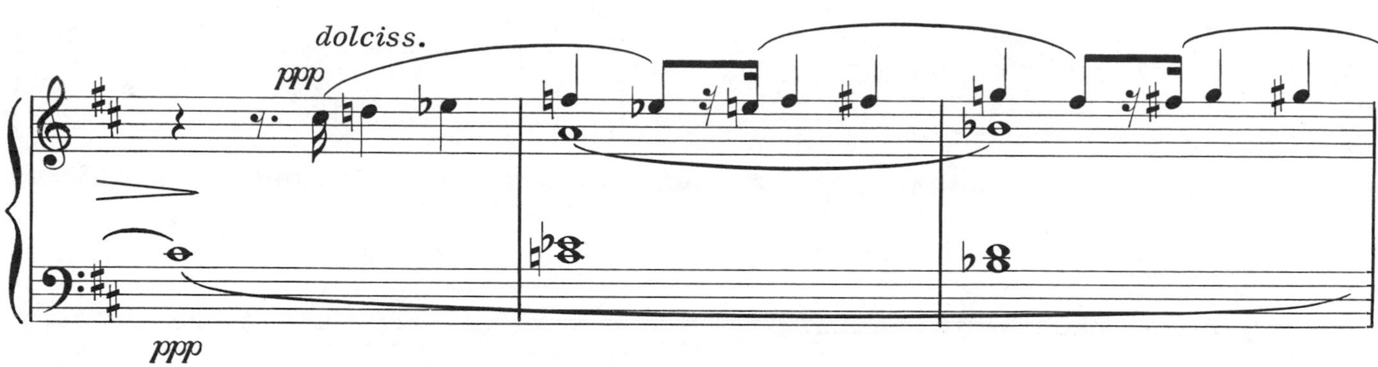
dolciss.
ppp
ppp

dolce

mf
incalzando e cresc.

cresc. molto

fff
dim.
ppp
pppp
ppp
pp
morendo
8

Act I

Act I

Scene I

Characters in Order of Appearance: Ramphis and Radames; Amneris; Aida; King; Messenger; Ministers; Priests; Soldiers, etc.

War is imminent. When the curtain rises on the quiet introductory exchange between Ramphis and Radames as they meet in a great hall in the Pharoh's palace at Memphis, the goddess Isis has already named the officer who will command the Egyptian forces in the fight against the Ethiopians. The priest takes to watch Radames closely as he tells the warrior of this, then leaves to report to the King that the goddess has made her choice.

Radames, now alone among the columns and statues, delivers a straightforward soliloquy revealing his direct and upright character, ambitions and expectations. Accompanied by trumpets and trombones, he first dares voice his hope that he the one chosen by Isis to lead the Egyptian army.

When quite suddenly contrasting these martial dreams with confessions of his love for "Celeste Aida", he sings of his longings to restore the captive to her homeland, the flutes arranged to suggest Ethiopia's heady tropic fragrances. This aria, when sung properly, is intended to have a daydream effect.

Celeste Aida
(Heavenly Aida)

RADAMES

Celeste Aida, forma divina, mistico serto di luce e fior, del mio pensiero tu sei regina, tu di mia vita sei lo splendor. Il tuo bel cielo vorrei ridarti, le dolci brezze del patrio suol . . . un regal serto sul crin posarti, ergerti un trono vicino al sol. Ah! Celeste Aida, forma divina, mistico raggio di luce e fior, ecc.	Heavenly Aida, divine form, mystical garland of light and flowers, you are the queen of my thoughts, you are the light of my life. I would return you your lovely sky, the gentle breezes of your native land . . . I would set a royal crown upon your head and build you a throne next the sun. Ah! Heavenly Aida, form divine, mystical ray of light and flowers, *etc.*

dolce
vi - na, mi - sti - co - ser - to
pp
di lu - ce e fior, del mio pen-
portate la voce
sie - ro tu sei re - gi - na, tu di mia

vi - ta sei lo splen - dor.
p espress.

sempre dolciss.
Il tuo bel cie - lo vor-rei ri - dar - ti, le dol- ci

animando un poco
brez - ze del pa - trio suol: un re - gal

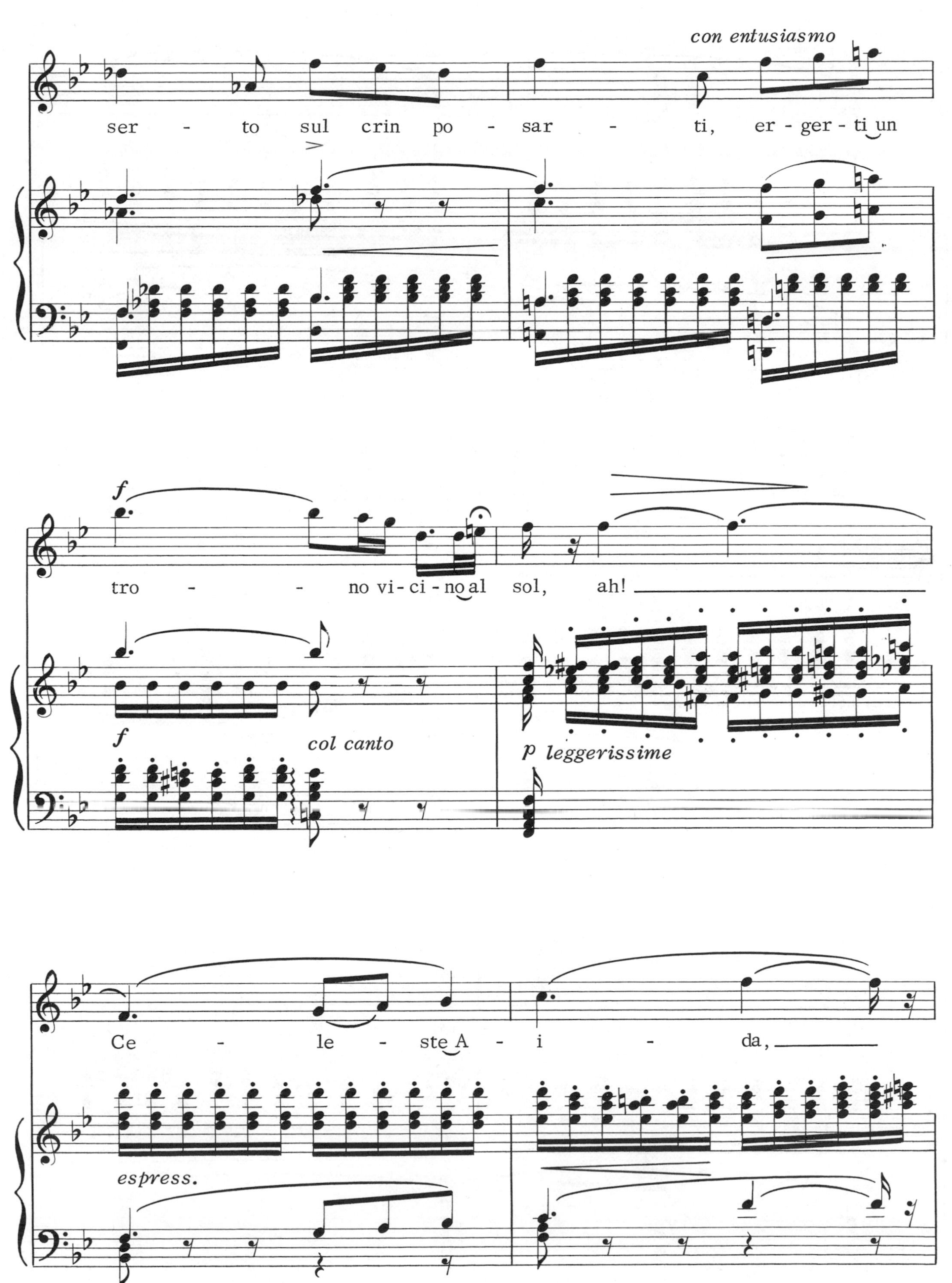
con entusiasmo
ser - to sul crin po - sar - ti, er - ger - ti un
tro - - no vi - ci - no al sol, ah!
f
f
col canto
p leggerissime
Ce - le - ste A - i - da,
espress.

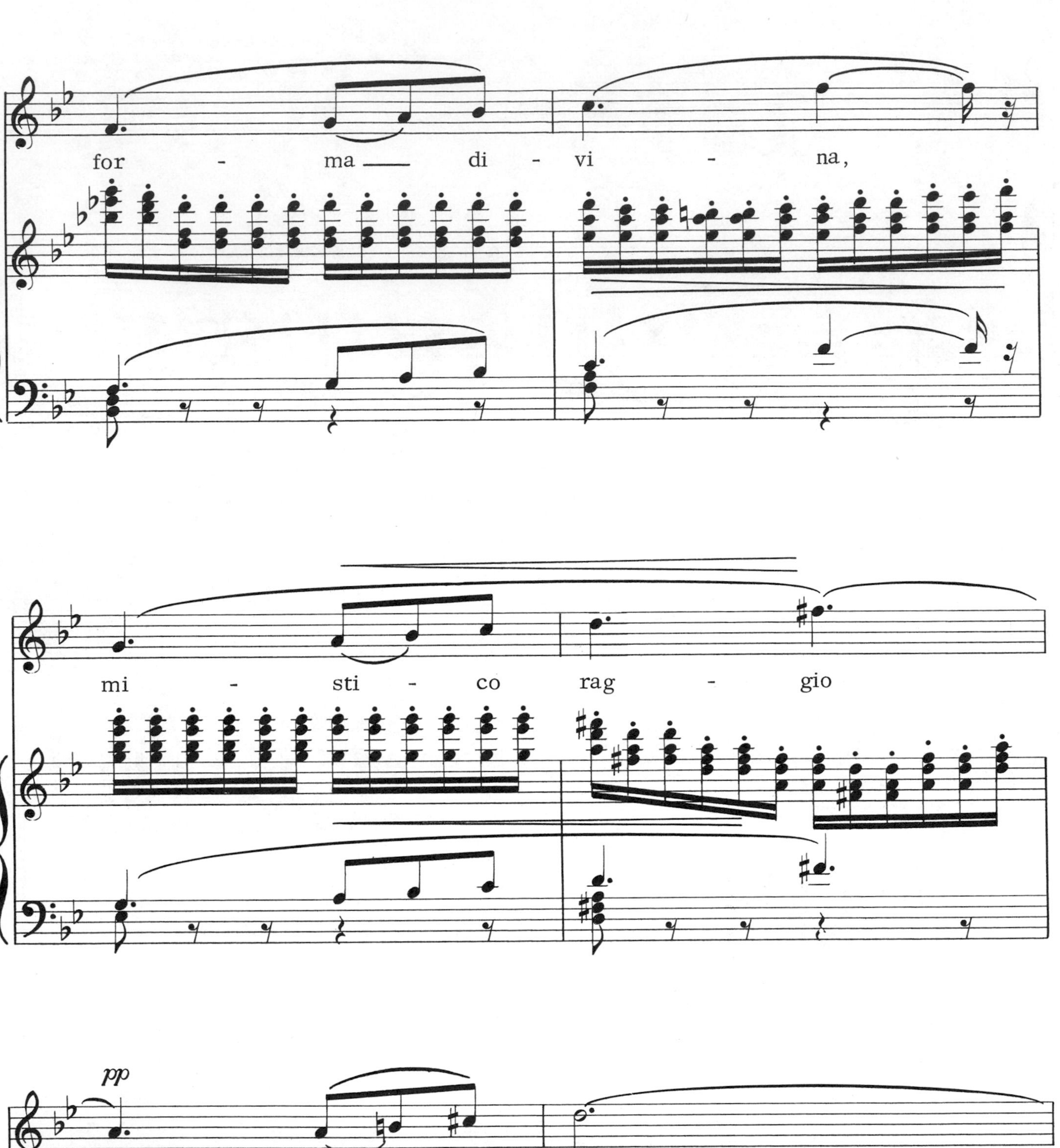

for - ma di - vi - na,

mi - sti - co rag - gio

del mio pen - sie - ro
tu sei re - gi - na, tu di mia
vi - ta sei lo splen - dor.
p
p

parlante ppp
Il tuo bel cie - lo vor-rei ri - dar - ti, le dol-ci brez - ze del pa-trio
ancora p
animando
f
suol; un re-gal ser - to sul crin po - sar - ti, er - ger-ti un
ancora p
pppp
ppp
dim.
tro-no vi-ci-no al sol, un tro-no vi-ci-no al sol, un tro - no vi-ci-no al
8
tr
tr
p
ppp

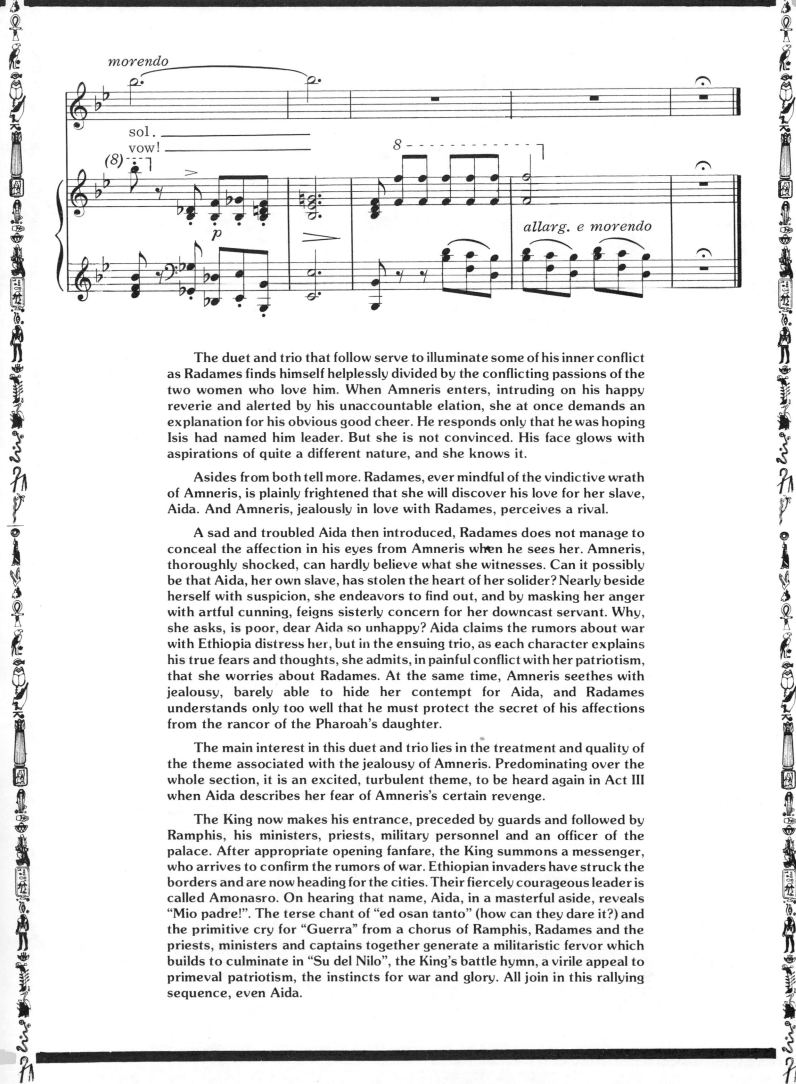

The duet and trio that follow serve to illuminate some of his inner conflict as Radames finds himself helplessly divided by the conflicting passions of the two women who love him. When Amneris enters, intruding on his happy reverie and alerted by his unaccountable elation, she at once demands an explanation for his obvious good cheer. He responds only that he was hoping Isis had named him leader. But she is not convinced. His face glows with aspirations of quite a different nature, and she knows it.

Asides from both tell more. Radames, ever mindful of the vindictive wrath of Amneris, is plainly frightened that she will discover his love for her slave, Aida. And Amneris, jealously in love with Radames, perceives a rival.

A sad and troubled Aida then introduced, Radames does not manage to conceal the affection in his eyes from Amneris when he sees her. Amneris, thoroughly shocked, can hardly believe what she witnesses. Can it possibly be that Aida, her own slave, has stolen the heart of her solider? Nearly beside herself with suspicion, she endeavors to find out, and by masking her anger with artful cunning, feigns sisterly concern for her downcast servant. Why, she asks, is poor, dear Aida so unhappy? Aida claims the rumors about war with Ethiopia distress her, but in the ensuing trio, as each character explains his true fears and thoughts, she admits, in painful conflict with her patriotism, that she worries about Radames. At the same time, Amneris seethes with jealousy, barely able to hide her contempt for Aida, and Radames understands only too well that he must protect the secret of his affections from the rancor of the Pharoah's daughter.

The main interest in this duet and trio lies in the treatment and quality of the theme associated with the jealousy of Amneris. Predominating over the whole section, it is an excited, turbulent theme, to be heard again in Act III when Aida describes her fear of Amneris's certain revenge.

The King now makes his entrance, preceded by guards and followed by Ramphis, his ministers, priests, military personnel and an officer of the palace. After appropriate opening fanfare, the King summons a messenger, who arrives to confirm the rumors of war. Ethiopian invaders have struck the borders and are now heading for the cities. Their fiercely courageous leader is called Amonasro. On hearing that name, Aida, in a masterful aside, reveals "Mio padre!". The terse chant of "ed osan tanto" (how can they dare it?) and the primitive cry for "Guerra" from a chorus of Ramphis, Radames and the priests, ministers and captains together generate a militaristic fervor which builds to culminate in "Su del Nilo", the King's battle hymn, a virile appeal to primeval patriotism, the instincts for war and glory. All join in this rallying sequence, even Aida.

Su! del Nilo al sacro lido
(Arise! To the sacred banks of the Nile)

MINISTERS *and* CAPTAINS

Su! del	Arise!
Nilo al sacro lido	To the sacred banks of the Nile
sien barriera i nostri petti;	let our breasts form a barrier;
non echeggi che un sol grido:	let there resound but a single cry:
guerra, guerra e morte	war, war and death
allo stranier!	to the foreigner!

RAMFIS

Ognun rammenti	Let everyone remember
che in poter dei numi solo	that the warrior's fortunes
stan le sorti del guerra!	rest solely in the hands of the gods!

KING

Su! su! del Nilo al sacro lido	Arise! Arise! Speed to the sacred
accorrete, egizii eroi.	banks of the Nile, Egyptian heroes.
Da ogni cor prorompa un grido:	Let the cry resound from every heart:
guerra e morte allo stranier!	war and death to the foreigner!

Allegro maestoso
THE KING
marc. assai
Su! del
ff
mf

Ni - lo al sa - cro li - do ac - cor - re - te E-gi - zii e -

roi, da o-gni cor pro-rom-pa il gri - do: guer - ra e

RAMPHIS
mor - te, mor - te allo stra - nier! Glo - ria ai
3
3
ff
mf

Nu - mi! O - gnun ram - men - ti ch'es si reg - go - no gli e -

ven - ti, che in po - ter d'e Nu - mi so - lo stan le
3
3

CHORUS f
sor - ti del guer - rier, Su! del
f
3

Ni - lo al sa - cro li - do sien bar -

rie - ra i no - stri pet - ti; non ec -

cheg - gi che un sol gri - do: guer - ra,

guer - ra e mor - te al-lo stra - nier!
3
3
tempo
ff

Verdi's technical ingenuity in this scene is such as to create a stunning excitement. The impact of Aida's contrapuntal misery is intensified when Radames takes up the tune in C Major; the cry for war is returned to as a kind of coda, and the climax is held back on the chord of the 7th.

Aida, moments ago swept up in the fervor of the now dispersed crowd, remains alone on stage to deliver her soliloquy. She had joined in the impassioned cries for Radames's victorious return, and begins her aria by dramatically repeating "Ritorno Vincitor!", the last phrase of the preceeding chorus. Catching herself in her treason at once, she recovers to bewail her impossible position, caught between country and heart. How can it be that the daughter of Amonasro, the King of Ethiopia, loves so deeply the confirmed enemy of her people? But it is only his love that has made her slavery in Egypt tolerable. She cannot renounce him, and voices her despair, growing ever more bleak, in the somber "Vincitor de' miei fratelli" passage, accompanied by cellos, oboe and bassoon. Who can she pray for? Who does she cry for? Her final, agonizing "Numi pieta" dissolves into uncontrollable tears. Lost in her confused self-condemnation, Aida has only the gods to plead with for pity and relief from her sufferings.

Ritorna vincitor!
(Return a conqueror!)

Ritorna vincitor! E dal mio labbro
usci l'empia parola!
Vincitor del padre mio . . . di lui
che impugna l'armi per me . . .
per ridonarmi una patria, una reggia
e il nome illustre
che qui celar m'e forza!
Vincitor de' miei fratelli . . .
ond'io lo vegga,
tinto del sangue amato,
trionfar nel plauso
dell'egizie coorti!
E dietro il carro, un re . . .
mio padre . . . di catene avvinto!
L'insana parola
o numi, sperdete!
Al seno d'un padre
la figlia rendete;
struggete, struggete,
struggete le squadre
dei nostri oppressor!
Ah, sventurata! che dissi?
e l'amor mio?
Dunque scordar poss'io
questo fervido amore
che, oppressa e schiava,
come raggio di sol
qui mi beava?
Imprechero la morte
a Radames . . .
a lui ch'amo pur tanto!
Ah! non fu in terra mai
da piu crudeli angoscie
un core affranto!
I sacri nomi di padre, d'amante
ne proferir poss'io, ne ricordar.
Per l'un, per l'altro,
confusa, tremante,
io piangere vorrei, vorrei pregar.
Ma la mia prece
in bestemmia si muta,
delitto e il pianto a me,
colpa il sospir.
In notte cupa
la mente e perduta,
e nell'ansia crudel
vorrei morir.
Numi, pieta del mio soffrir!
Speme non v'ha pel mio dolor.
Amor fatal, tremendo amor
spezzami il cor, fammi morir!
Numi, pieta del mio soffrir! *ecc.*

Return a conqueror! And from my lips
came the unholy word!
Conqueror of my father . . . of him
who bears arms for me . . .
to restore a country, a kingdom,
and the illustrious name
that I am forced to hide!
Conqueror of my brothers . . .
whence I might see him,
stained with cherished blood,
triumph in the boasting
of the Egyptian cohorts!
And behind his chariot, a king . . .
my father . . . bound in chains!
O gods, vanish
the insane word!
Restore a daughter
to her father's breast;
destroy, destroy,
destroy the forces
of our oppressor!
Ah, wretched one! What did I say?
And my love?
Can I then forget
this fervent love
which, like a shaft of sunlight,
delighted me here
although I am captive and a slave?
Shall I call down death
upon Radames . . .
upon him whom I love so dearly!
Ah! never on earth did
anguish more cruel
tear apart a heart!
I cannot utter, nor yet recall
The sacred names of father, of lover.
For the one, for the other,
confused, trembling,
I would weep, I would pray.
But my prayer
turns to blasphemy;
for me tears are a crime,
sighs a fault.
In darkest night
my soul is lost,
and in this cruel anguish
I would die.
O gods, have pity on my suffering!
There is no hope for my sorrow.
Fatal love, boundless love,
break my heart, let me die!
O gods, take pity on my suffering! *etc.*

Allegro agitato
Ri-tor-na vin-ci -tor!
E dal mio lab - bro u-
ff
pp

sci l'em - pia pa - ro - la!
Vin- ci-
f

tor del pa - dre mi - o di lui che im - pu - gna l'ar - mi per
pp

3
3
me per ri - do - nar - mi u - na pa - tria, u-na reg - gia e il no-me il
lu - stre che qui ce-lar m'è for-za! Vin - ci -
f
tor de' miei fra - tel - li on - d'io lo
pp

veg - ga, tin - to del san - que a - ma - to,

tri-on-far nel plau - - so dell' E-gi-zie co-
cresc.

or - ti! E die-tro il car - ro, un Re mio

pa - dre di ca - te - ne av - vin - to!
ff

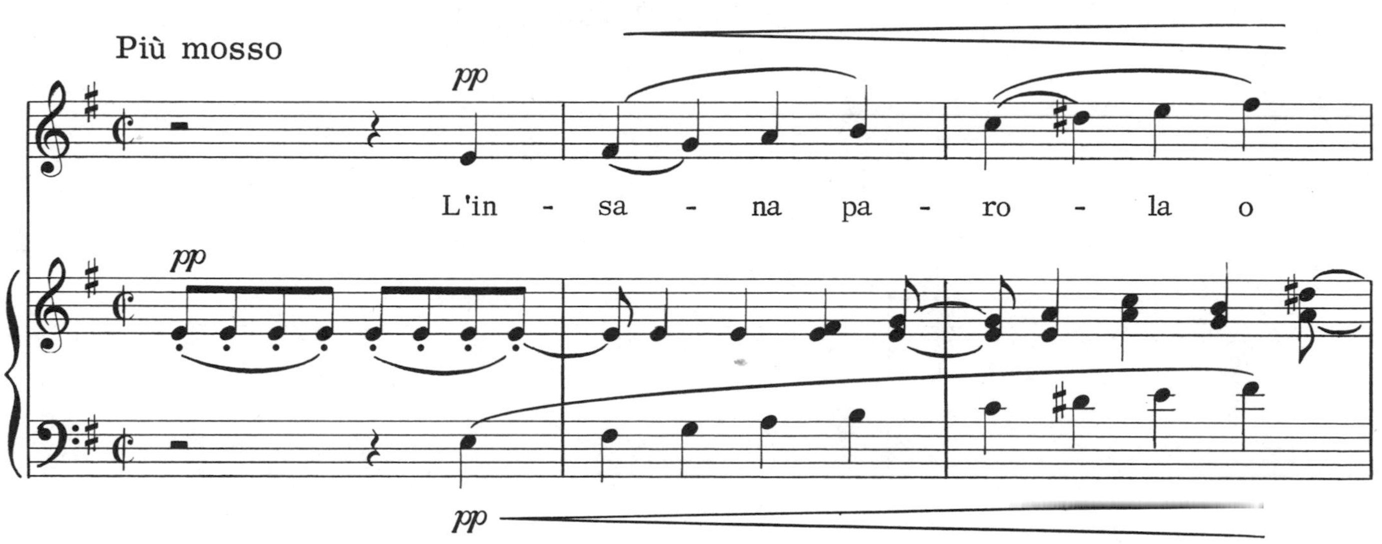
Più mosso
pp
L'in - sa - na pa - ro - la o
pp
pp

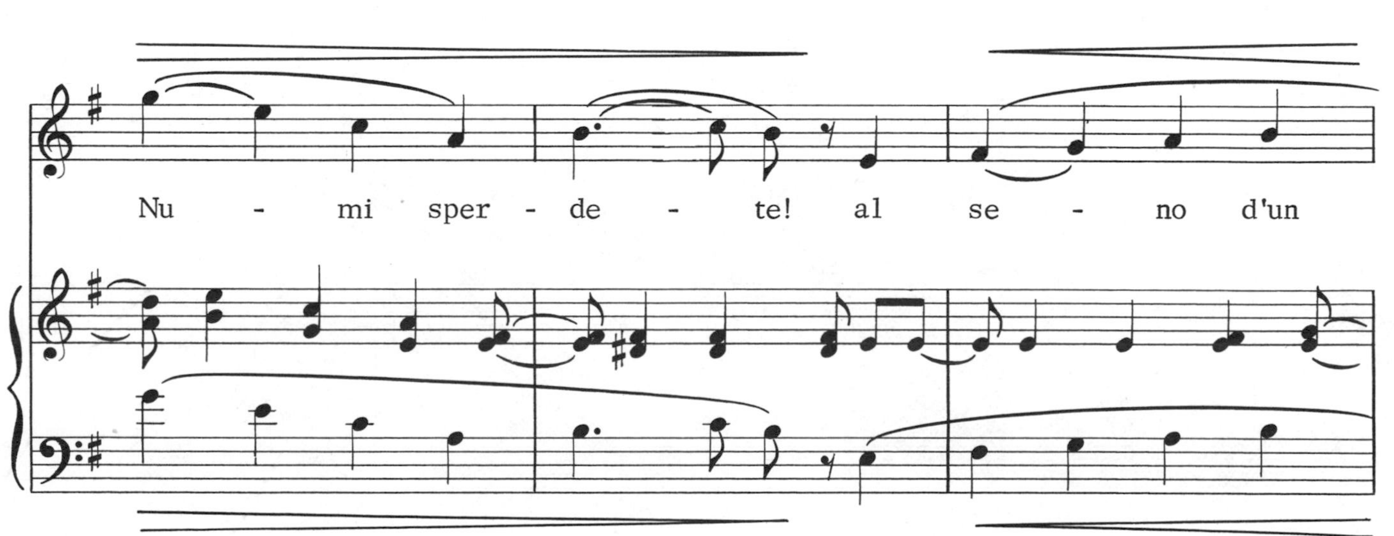
Nu - mi sper - de - te! al se - no d'un

pa - dre la fi - glia ren - de - te, strug - ge - -
f

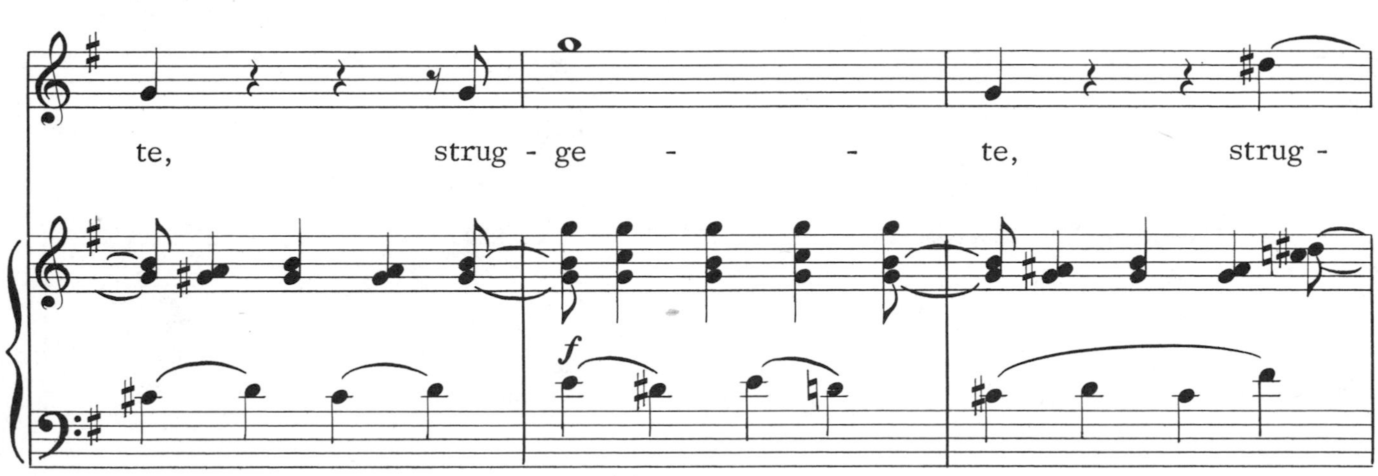
te, strug - ge - - te, strug -
f

ge - te le squa - dre dei no - stri op - pres - sor!

ff
Ah! sven-tu - ra - ta! che
ff

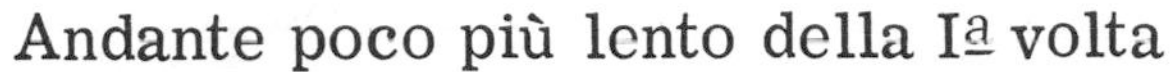

Andante poco più lento della Iª volta

dis - si? e l'a - mor mi - o?
3
p cantabile
pp

Dun - que scor - dar pos - s'i - o que - sto fer - vi - do a -

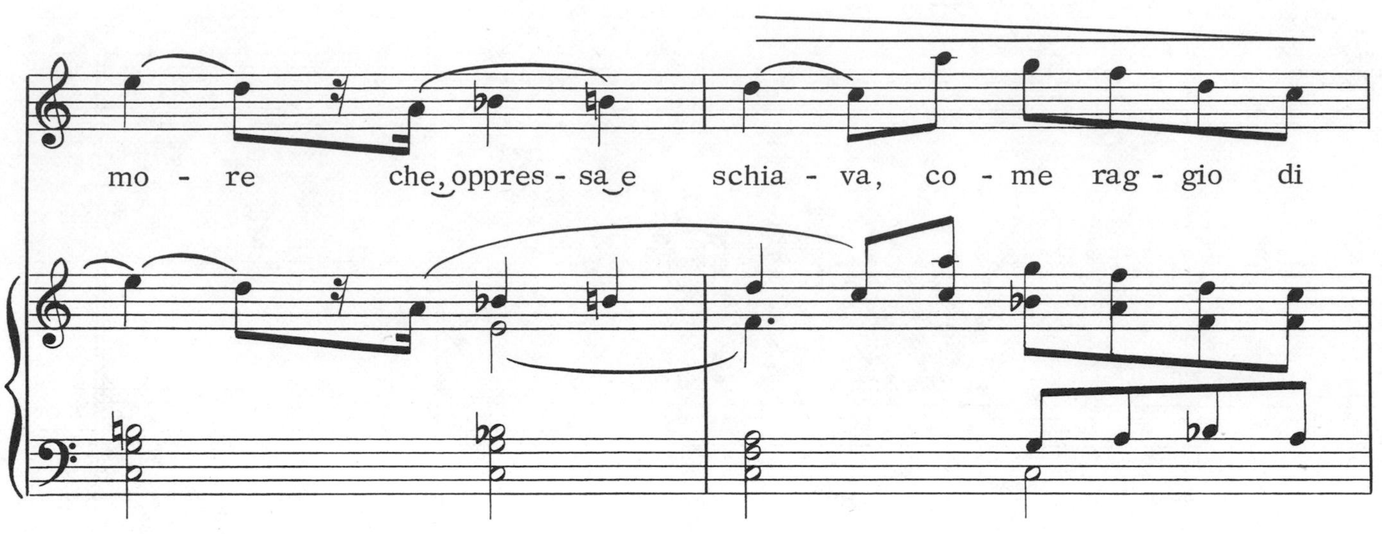
mo - re che oppres - sa e schia - va, co - me rag - gio di

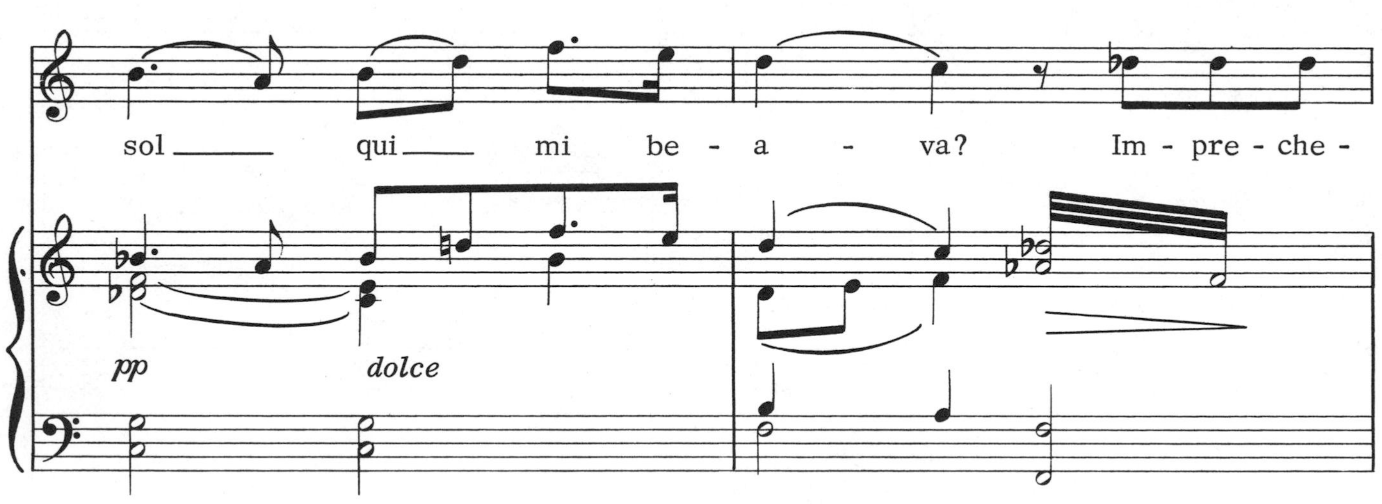
sol qui mi be - a - va? Im - pre - che -
pp
dolce

rò la mor - te a Ra - da - mès a lui ch'a - mo pur

f
3
3
tan - to!
Ah!
non fu in
ter - ra

3
3
3
3
mai
da più
cru - de -
- li an - go - scie un co - re af -
p

fran - to!.
rall.
morendo

Allegro giusto poco agitato

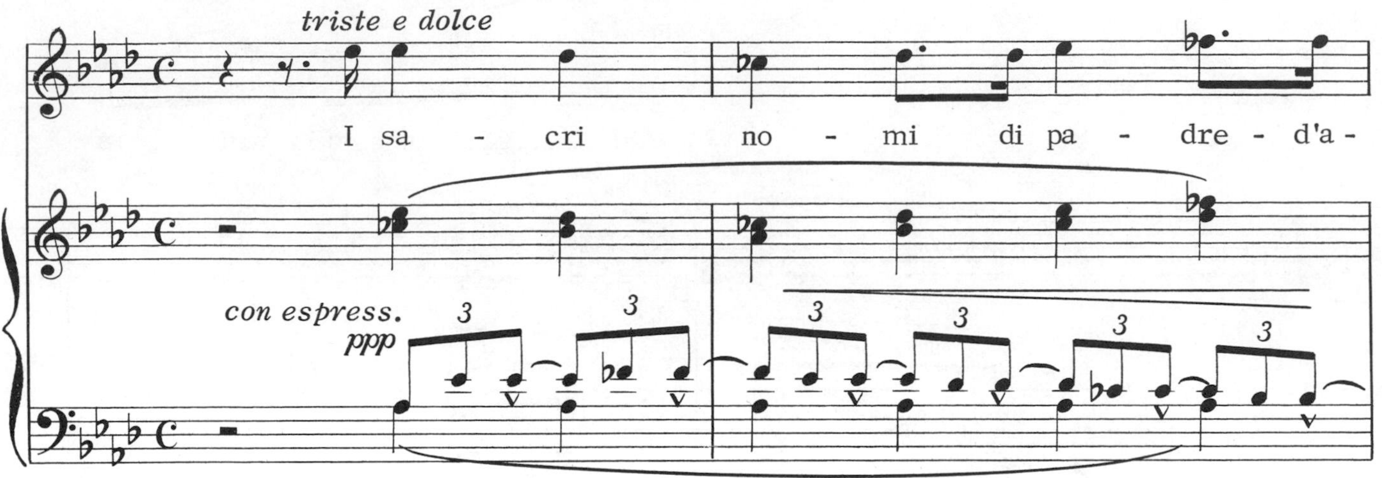

man-te io pian-ge-re vor-rei vor-rei pre-
l.h.

con più forza
gar. Ma la mia pre-ce in bestem-mia si
p

mu-ta de-lit-to e il pian-to a me col-pa il so-

spir in not - te cu - pa la men - te è per-
3
p
3
du - ta e nell' an - sia cru - del vor - rei mo-
3
3
Cantabile
con espress.
rir Nu - mi, pie - tà

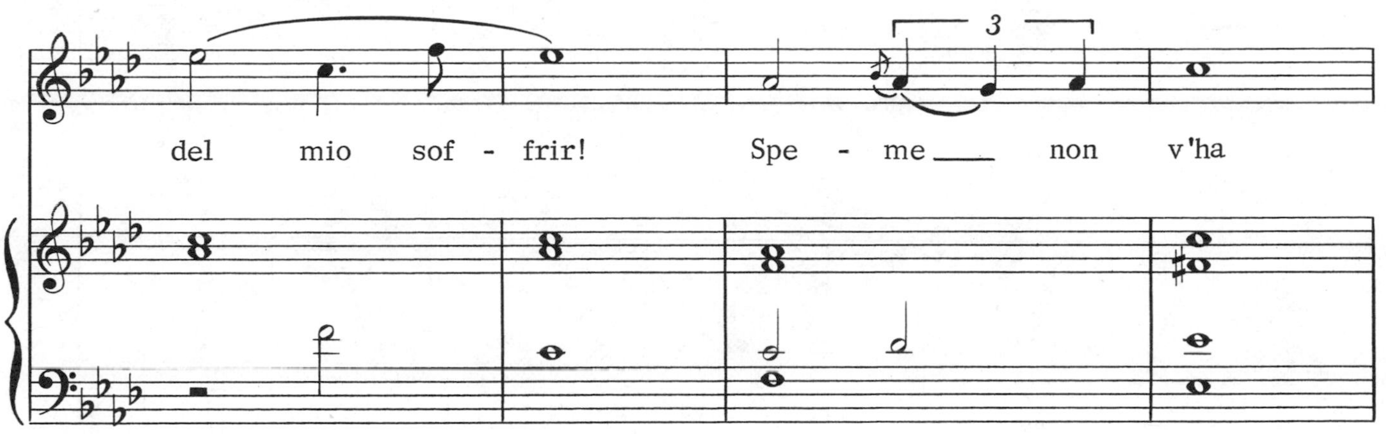
3
del mio sof - frir! Spe - me non v'ha

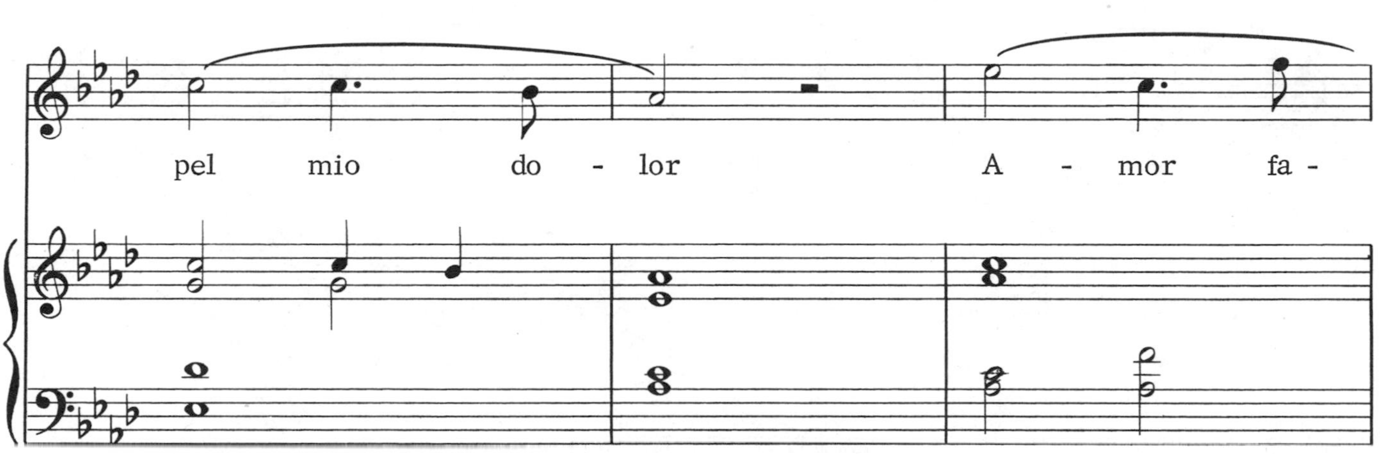
pel mio do - lor A - mor fa -

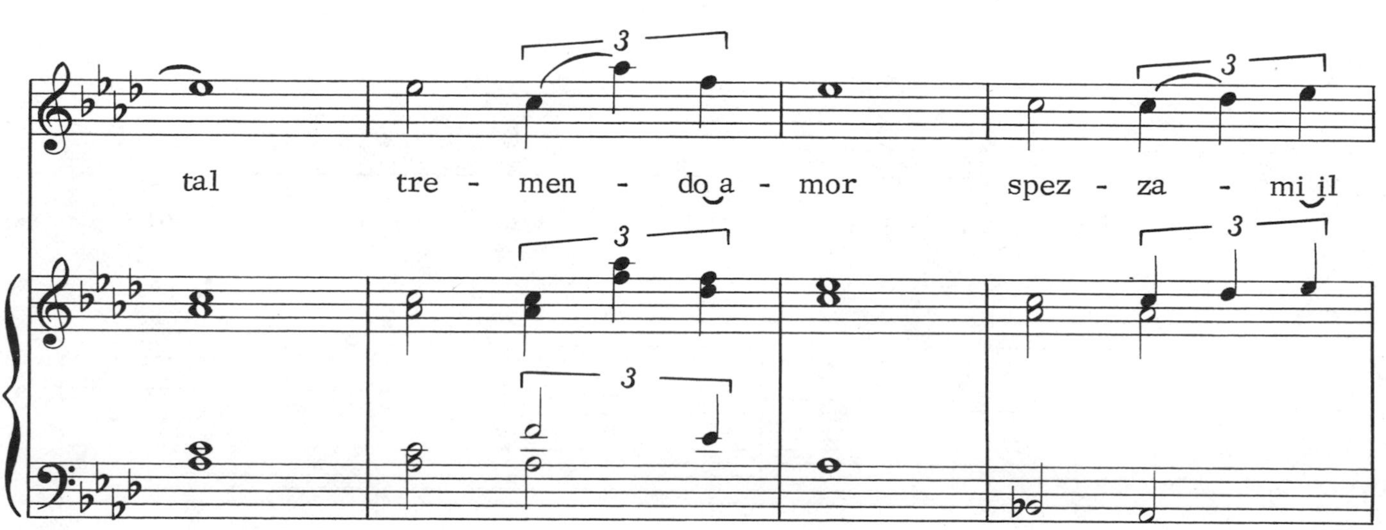
3
3
tal tre - men - do a - mor spez - za - mi il
3
3

p
cor, fam - mi mo - rir! Nu - mi, pie -

poco string.
tà del mio sof - frir, ah! pie -

tà, Nu - mi, pie - tà del mio sof -

frir, Nu - mi, pie - tà del mio sof -
f
frir, pie - tà, pie - tà del
pp
ppp
perdendosi
mio sof - frir!
dolce
morendo
ppp
morendo

Act I, Scene II
Characters in Order of Appearance: Ramphis, Priests and Priestesses; Radames.

The atmospheric setting for this Consecration Scene was conscientiously researched. The result is entirely theatrical and absolutely convincing. The lighting is indirect, dim, the air heavy with incense. Dominating a temple dedicated to the worship of Vulcan, an ornate gilded altar surrounded by sacred statues and columns rises above the carpeted platform in the center of the stage. It is a short while later.

Based on three main musical concepts, the score in this scene is highly objective. The hieratic chant of the priestesses to Phtha, the first idea, deliberately eastern with its undulating rhythm and simple harp accompaniment, might well pass for authentic Egyptian music if Verdi had not admitted it was his own invention. This chorus alternates with the invocation of the priests, the second idea, the two heightening the solemnity and mystical properties of the scene.

Possente, possente Ftha,
(O mighty, mighty Ptah!)

High Priestess

Possente, possente Ftha, del mondo spirito animator, ah! . . .	O mighty, mighty Ptah! spirit that animates the world, ah! . . .

High Priestess *and* Priestesses

. . . noi t'invochiamo!	. . . we invoke thee!

Ramfis *and* Priests

Tu che dal nulla hai tratto l'onde, la terra, il ciel, noi t'invochiamo!	Thou who from nothingness did create The earth, the sea and the sky, we invoke thee!

High Priestess

Immenso, immenso Ftha, del mondo spirito fecondator, ah! . . .	Phtha most high, universal creator of life, ah! . . .

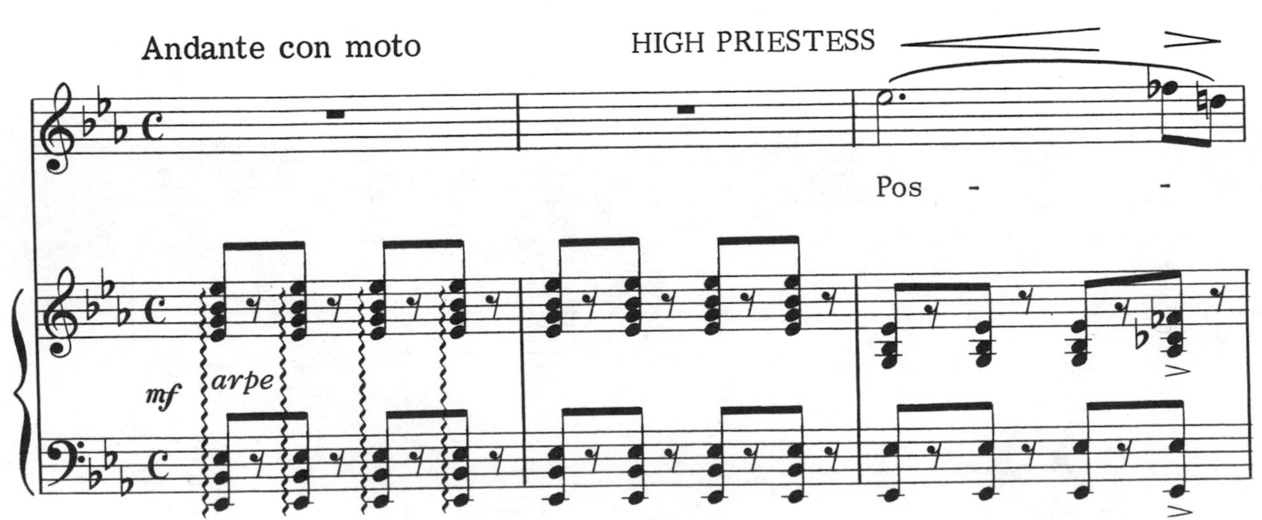

(forte l'appoggiatura)
sen - te, pos-sen - te Fthà, del mon - -

f
do spi-ri-to a - ni - ma - tor, ah! ah!
f
f

pp dim.
noi t'in-vo-chia - - mo!
pp
pp morendo col canto
etc.

Serving as a kind of intermezzo, the sacred dance of the priestesses that follows is perhaps the best such music ever written by Verdi. The theme is mainly carried by three flutes, whose trills and triplets manage to suggest the east without in any way being eastern. Radames, unarmed, enters the temple during this dance and approaches the altar. There a silver veil is placed on his head, and as the dancers finish their recital, Ramphis ceremonially places a sword in the chosen warrior's hands.

Sacred Dance of the Priestesses

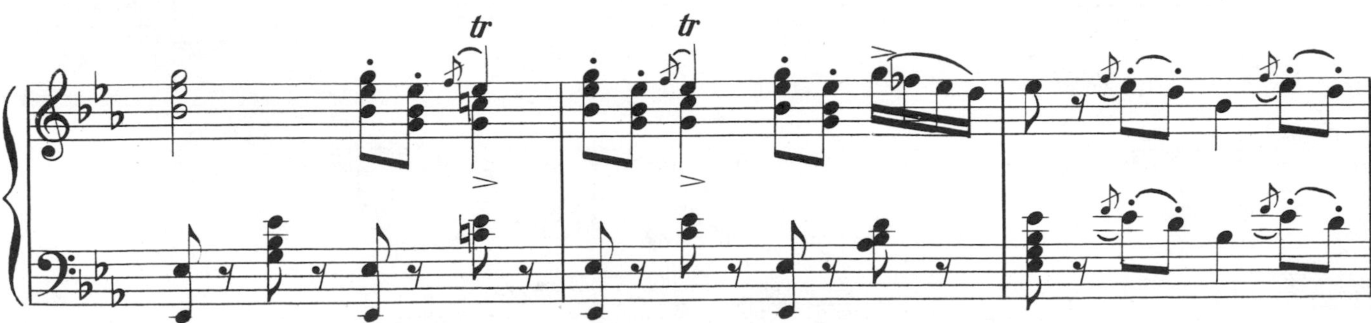

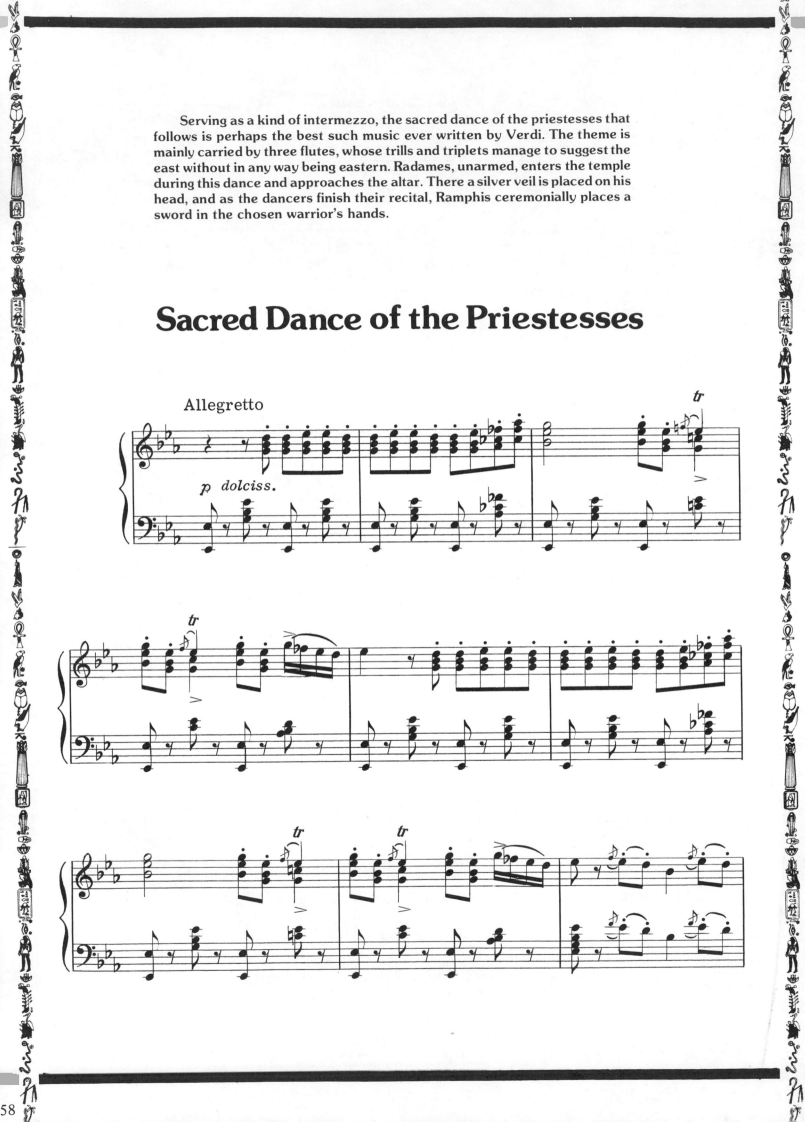

tr
l.h.
f

tr
pp
tr
tr
f
pp
leggero
tr
tr

The chanting now gives way to the broad theme of Ramphis as he turns to pray before his god. Radames joins him his prayers, and the ensemble at the conclusion of the scene combining all three ideas closes on all the worshippers joining in the sacred rituals.

Nume, custode ed arbitro

(O god, guardian and arbiter)

RAMFIS *and* PRIESTS

Nume, custode ed arbitro di questa sacra terra, *ecc.*	O god, guardian and arbiter of this sacred land, *etc.*

Act II

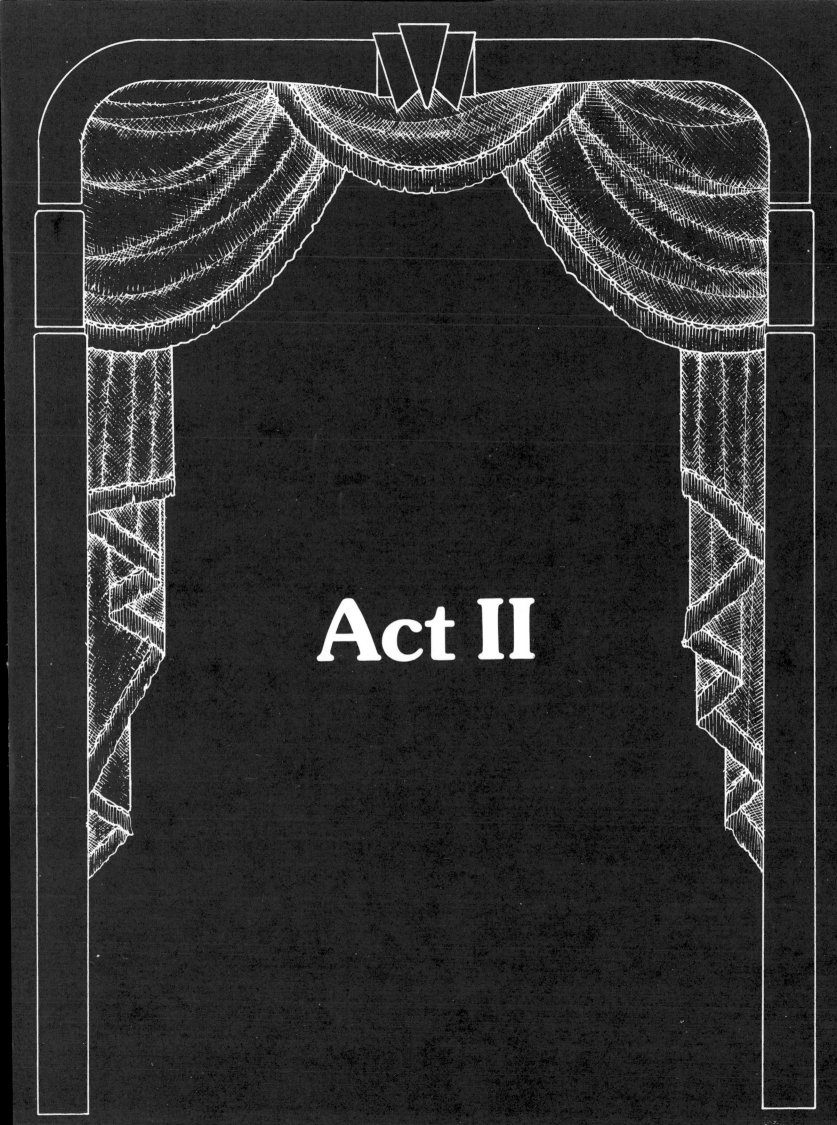

Act II

Scene I

Characters in Order of Appearance: Amneris and slaves; Aida.

This scene, in contrast to the second scene of Act I is essentially subjective, with small touches of theatricalism used only at the beginning and end. The emotional dispositions of the complicated Amneris and woe-riddled Aida are explored with great insight and technical skill. "Aida's Theme" is important here, but, interestingly, neither of the themes earlier associated with Amneris are present. She is translated into new terms, the music displaying her falseness, jealousy, anger and contempt for Aida with impressive originality.

It is some time later and the Egyptians have won their war as the scene opens on the opulent apartments of Amneris. Young Moorish slaves wave feather fans and a chorus of women sings of that great victory, bidding Radames to come and collect their mistress, Amneris. While other slavers help prepare her for the upcoming victors' banquet, Amneris, eager to serve as his reward for the triumph, sings of her lover, impatient for his return.

Chi mai, chi mai
(Who is it, who is it)

SLAVES

Chi mai, chi mai fra gl'inni e i plausi, erge alla gloria il vol, al par d'un dio terribile, fulgente al part del sol? Vieni: sul crin ti piovano contesti ai lauri i fior; suonin di gloria i cantici coi cantici d'amor.	Who is it, that amidst hymns and praises, soars to glory like a mighty god, shining like the sun? Come: let flowers laced with laurel shower upon your hair; let hymns of glory sound with songs of love.

AMNERIS

Ah! vieni, vieni, amor mio, m'inebbria, fammi beato il cor!	Ah, come, my love, enrapture me, fill my heart with happiness!

er - ge al - la glo - ria il— vol, al

par d'un Dio ter - ri - bi-le, ful-
pp

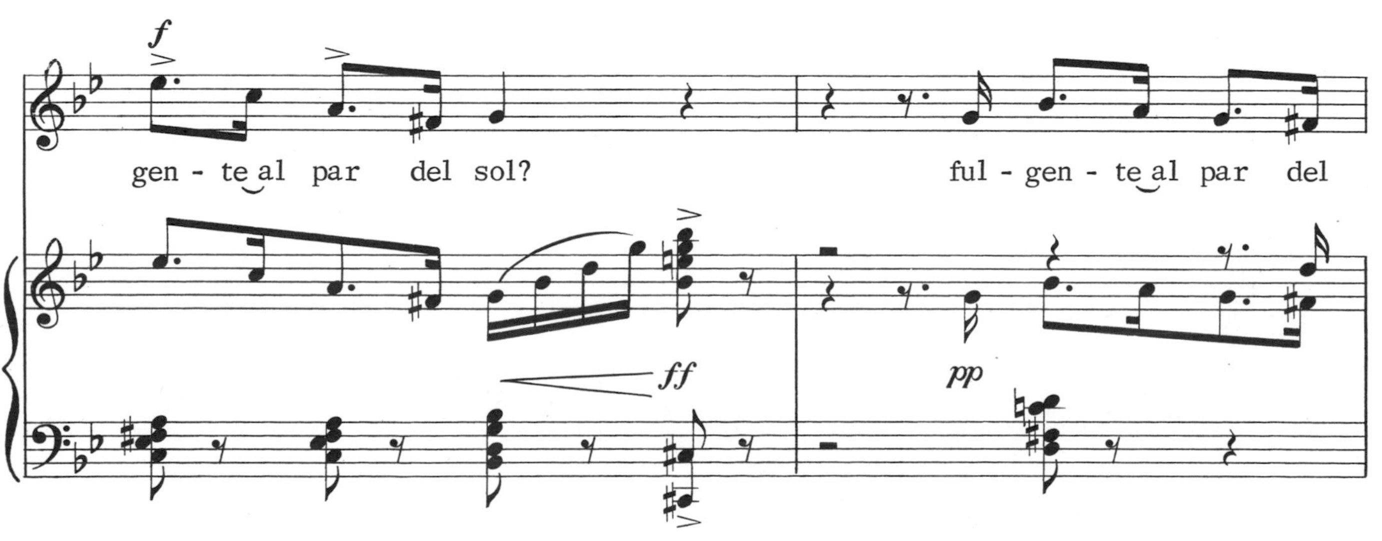
f
gen - te al par del sol? ful - gen - te al par del
ff
pp

sol?
Vie - ni: sul crin ti
8
3
dolciss.

pio - va - no
con - te - sti ai
pp

lau - ri, ai lau - ri i
fior; suo - nin di glo - ria i

can - ti - ci
coi can - ti - ci d'a -
pp

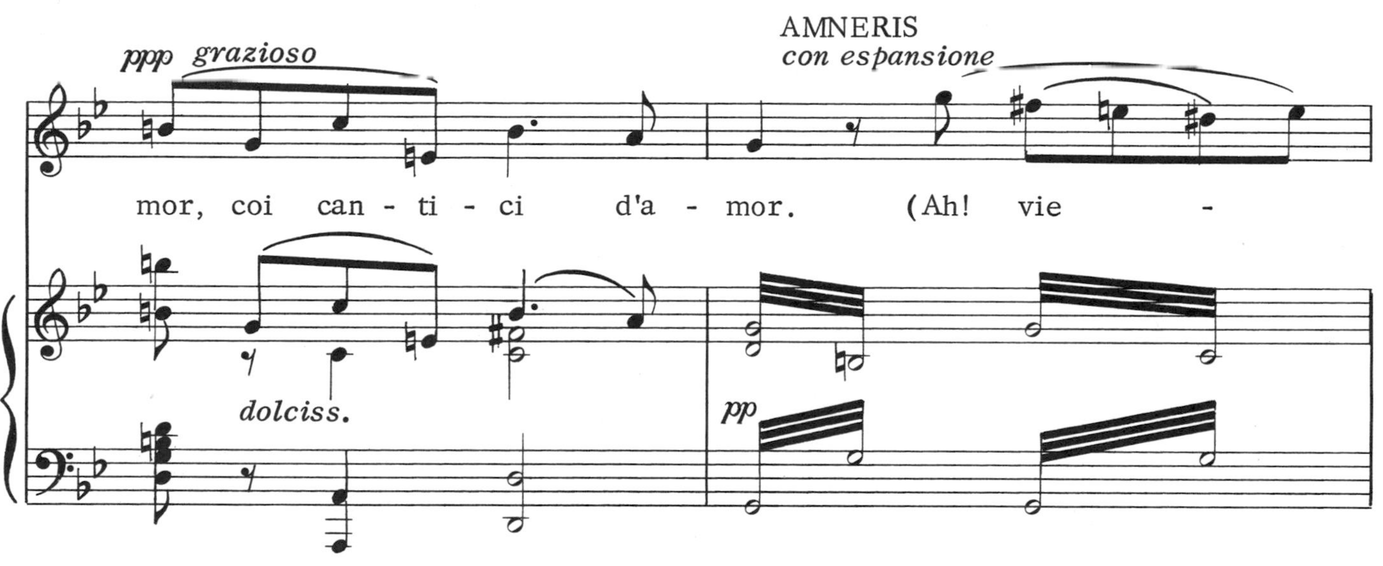
ppp grazioso
AMNERIS
con espansione
mor, coi can - ti - ci d'a - mor. (Ah! vie -
dolciss.
pp

ni, vie - ni a - mor mio, m'i - neb - bria, fam - mi be - a - to il

The slaves continue to ready Amneris for the feast while her Moorish vassels present their charming dance; its harmony and orchestration render it appealingly exotic. At the dance's conclusion, Amneris signals for the slaves to retire, and Aida arrives.

Dance of the Moorish Slaves

pp
pp

mf

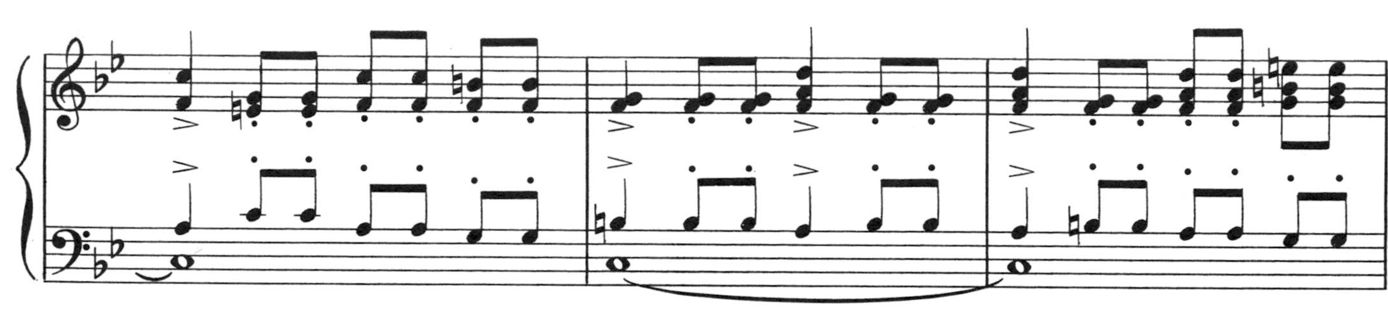

leggiero

pp
marcato

ff
f
ff

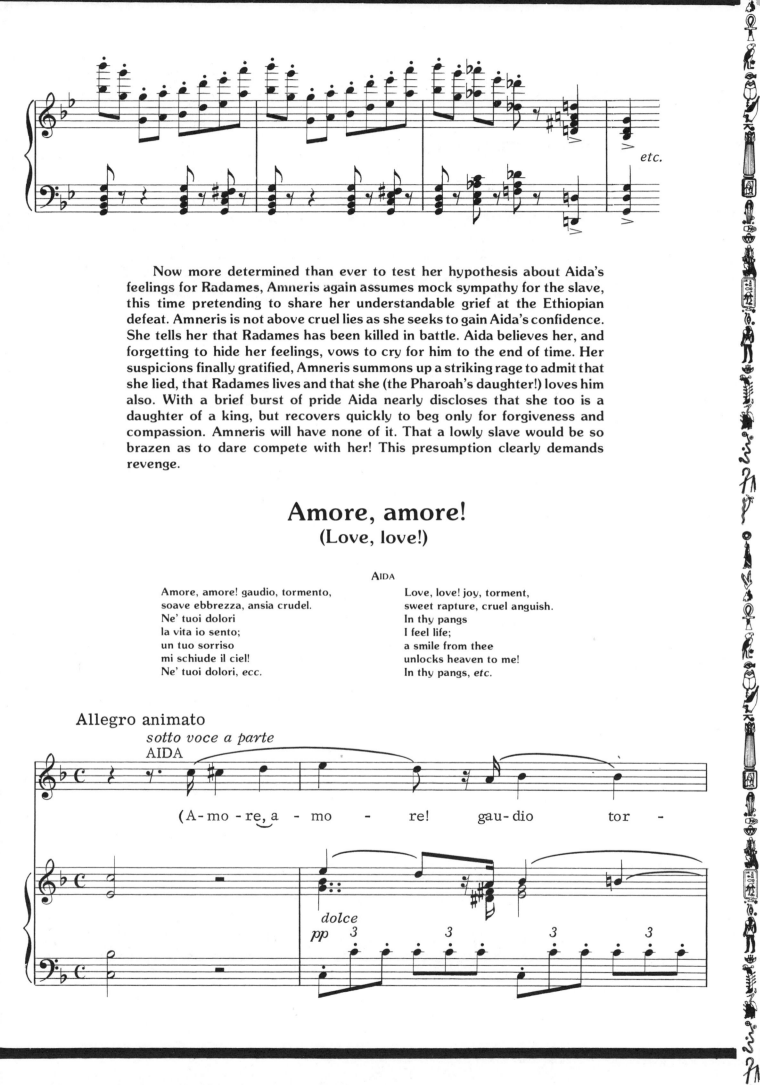

Now more determined than ever to test her hypothesis about Aida's feelings for Radames, Amneris again assumes mock sympathy for the slave, this time pretending to share her understandable grief at the Ethiopian defeat. Amneris is not above cruel lies as she seeks to gain Aida's confidence. She tells her that Radames has been killed in battle. Aida believes her, and forgetting to hide her feelings, vows to cry for him to the end of time. Her suspicions finally gratified, Amneris summons up a striking rage to admit that she lied, that Radames lives and that she (the Pharoah's daughter!) loves him also. With a brief burst of pride Aida nearly discloses that she too is a daughter of a king, but recovers quickly to beg only for forgiveness and compassion. Amneris will have none of it. That a lowly slave would be so brazen as to dare compete with her! This presumption clearly demands revenge.

Amore, amore!
(Love, love!)

AIDA

Amore, amore! gaudio, tormento, soave ebbrezza, ansia crudel. Ne' tuoi dolori la vita io sento; un tuo sorriso mi schiude il ciel! Ne' tuoi dolori, *ecc.*	Love, love! joy, torment, sweet rapture, cruel anguish. In thy pangs I feel life; a smile from thee unlocks heaven to me! In thy pangs, *etc.*

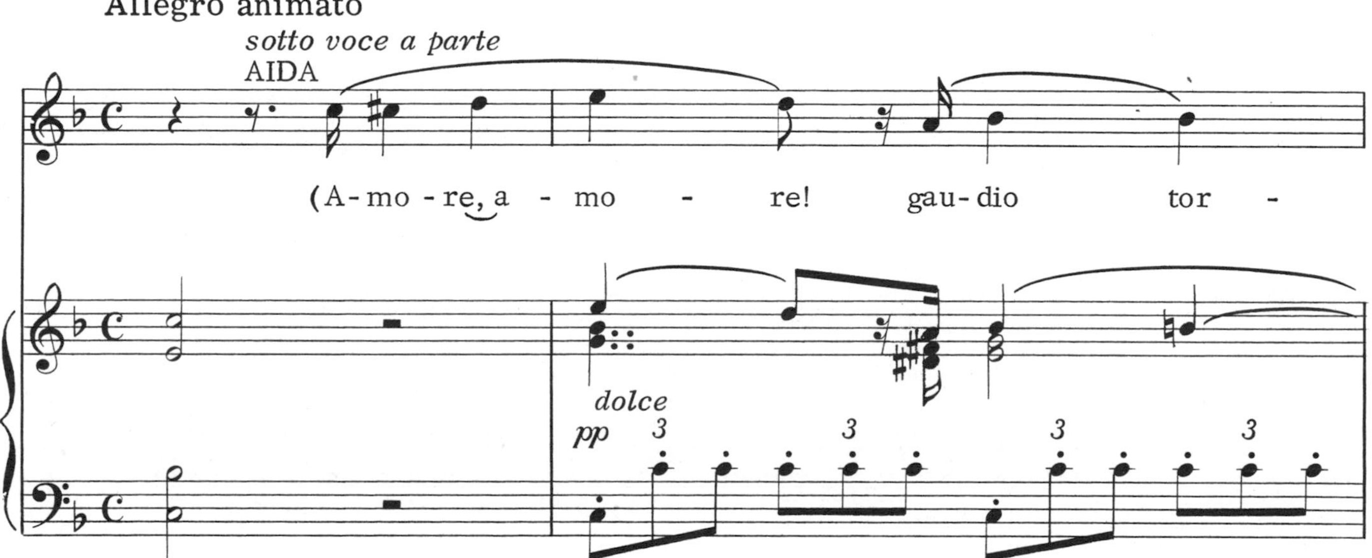

men - to so - a - ve eb - brez - za, an - sia cru-

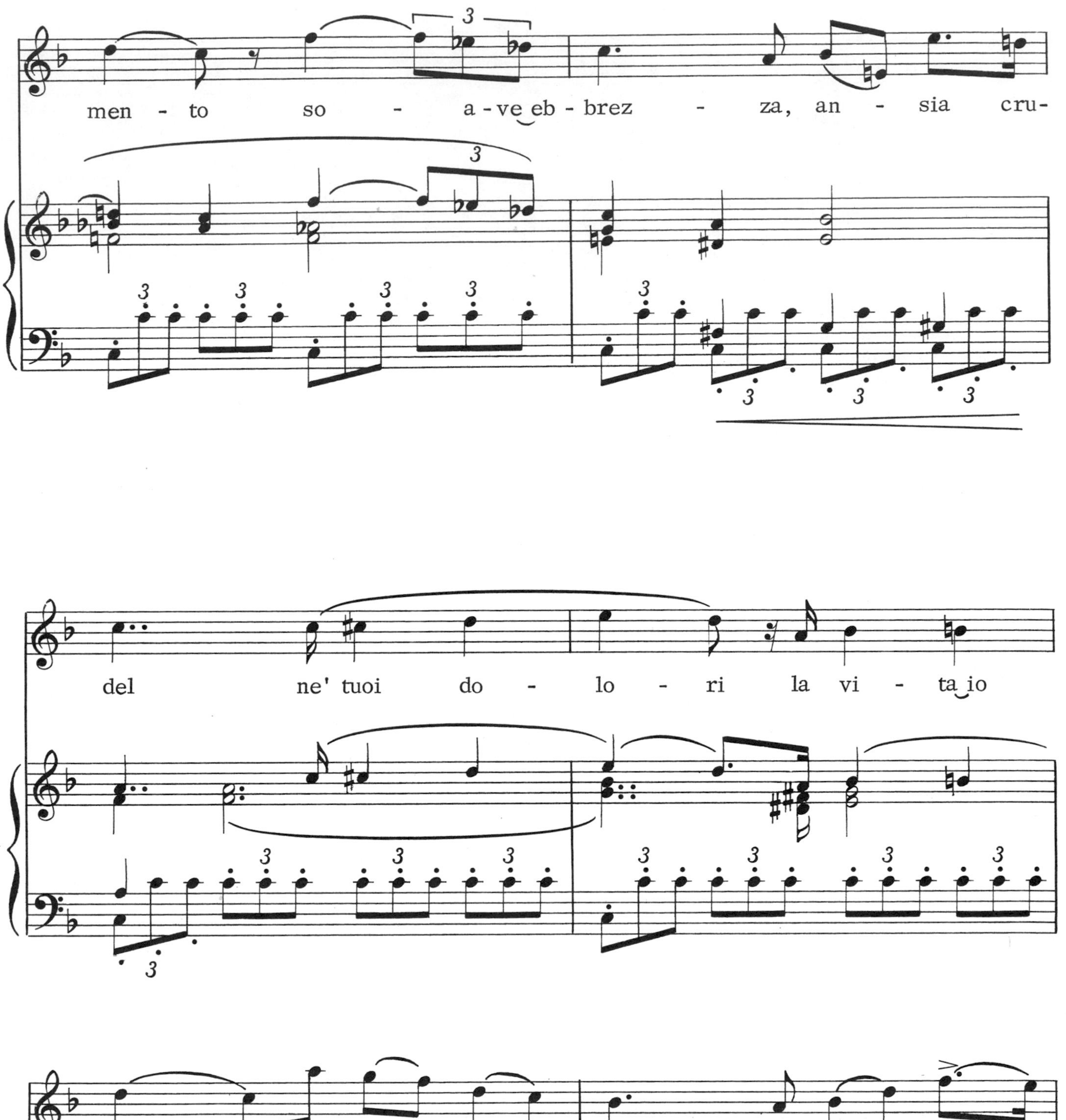

del ne' tuoi do - lo - ri la vi - ta io

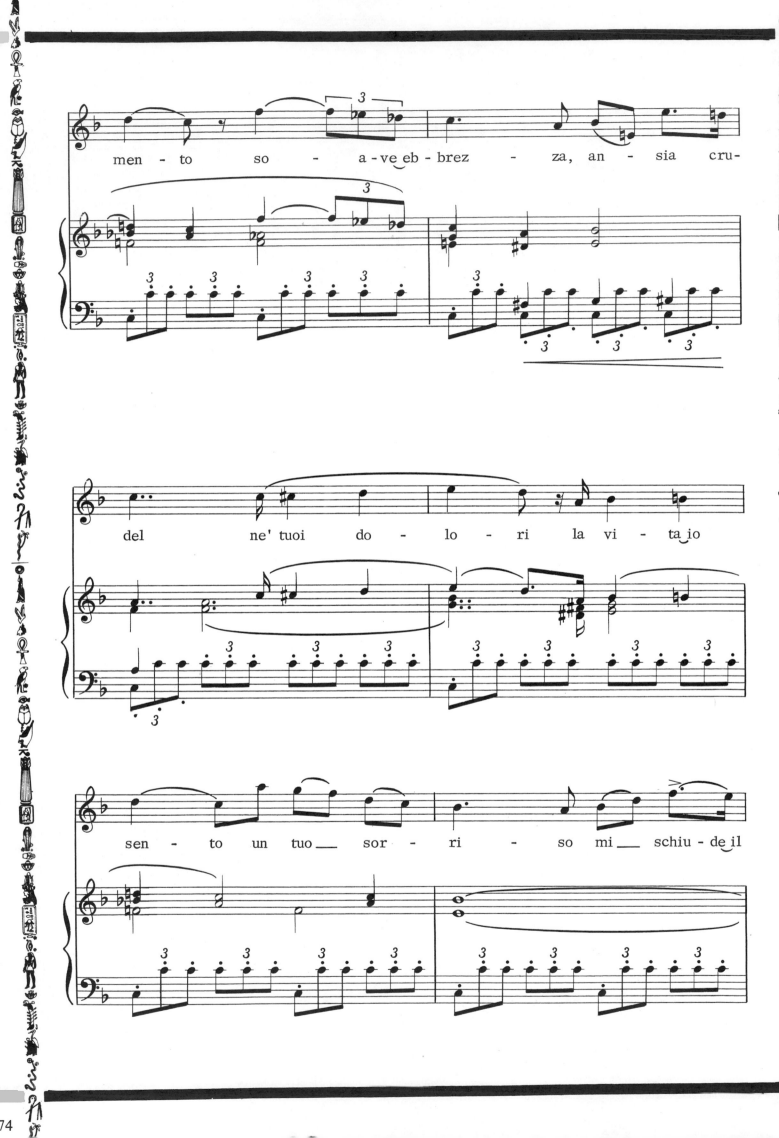

sen - to un tuo sor - ri - so mi schiu - de il

a poco a poco cresc.
ciel, un tuo sor-ri - so mi schiu-de il
pp leggeriss.

f
ciel, ne' tuoi do - lo - ri la vi - ta io
ff e string. poco a poco

sen - to un tuo sor - ri - so mi schiu - de il

Poco più lento
AMNERIS
ciel:)
Eb-ben: qual nuo - vo
espressivo
p

fer-mi-to t'as-sai, gen-til A - i - da?
I tuoi se-gre-ti
dolce

sve - la-mi, al - l'a - mor mi - o, al-l'a-mor mio t'af-
dolce

fi - da Tra i for - ti che pu - gna - ro - no del - la tua pa - tria a

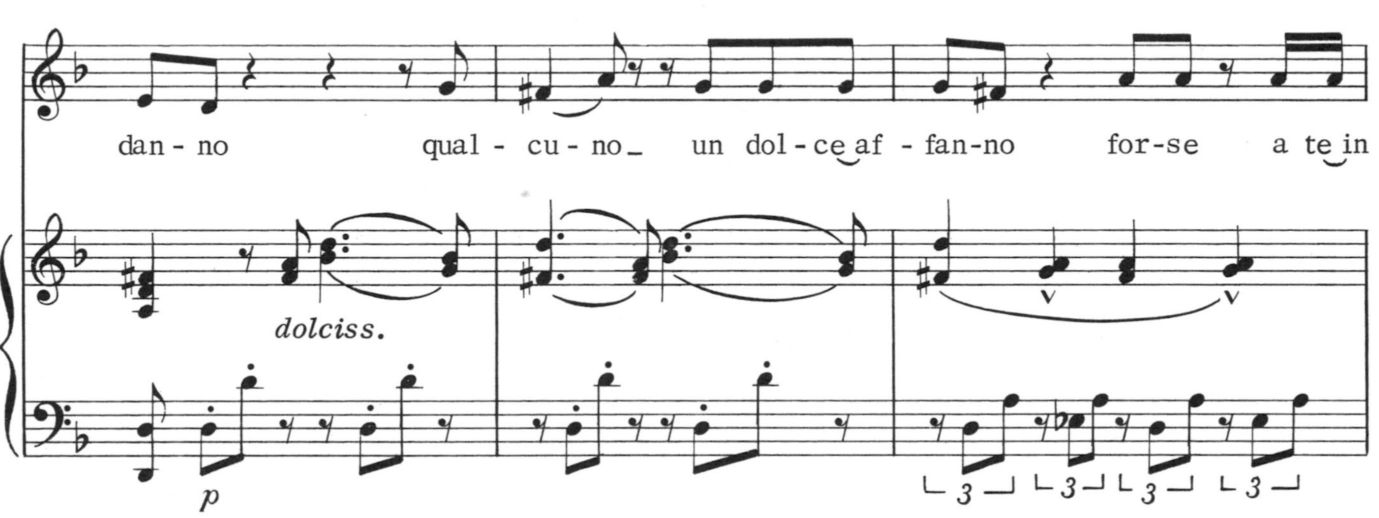
dan - no qual - cu - no un dol - ce af - fan - no for - se a te in
dolciss.
p
3 3 3 3

cor de - stò? A tut - ti bar - ba - ra non si mo - strò la
3 3 3 3

At this segment's conclusion, a chorus from outside chants of the triumph, while Aida, commanded by her mistress to follow after her and watch the return of the heroes, continues her appeal to the gods. While her music is not as good as that of Amneris in this scene, Aida's petition for mercy, "Ah pieta ti prenda", is a lovely melody, and with its expressive accompaniment on flutes, bassoon and clarinet, one of the scene's highlights.

Ah! pieta ti prenda del mio dolor.

(Ah! Have pity on my sorrow!)

AIDA

Ah! pieta ti prenda del mio dolor. E vero, io l'amo d'immenso amor. Tu sei felice, tu sei possente, io vivo solo per questo amor!	Ah! Have pity on my sorrow! It is true, I love him passionately. You are happy, you are powerful, I live only for this love!

lor E ve - ro, io l'a - mo d im-men - so a -
mor Tu sei fe - li - ce tu sei pos -
sen - te-io vi - vo so - lo per que - sto a -
mor!
3
etc.

Act II, Scene II

Characters in Order of Appearance: King, Amneris; Aida; Radames, Ramphis, Amonasro; Priests, Heralds, Citizens, Soldiers, Slaves, Captives, etc.

Taking place on a palm-lined avenue leading to the City of Thebes, a great deal happens during this purely theatrical and enormously crowded Triumphal Scene. The music is preoccupied with external effects, but is not without value or interest. With a flourish of suitable fanfare, the King enters in full state, attended by officials, priests, captains, fanbearers and standard bearers. He takes his place at a canopied throne; to his right stands a temple dedicated to Ammon and the Triumphal Arch is visible in the background. Amneris enters, followed by her slaves, including Aida, and is seated at her father's side.

Once chosen as the Egyptian National Anthem, the "Gloria all' Eggito" chorus with its brass band accompaniment is a spirited proclamation of the glory of the mighty sovereign, the country and the gods. At its completion, troops, scores of them, preceded by long trumpets, tramp on stage to defile before the King in the well-known and undeniably exciting Egyptian March passage. Its excitement is heightened by a trick of instrumentation, for the music is not only composed for two sets of trumpets differing in key, but the key itself shifts in the middle, directing attention to the sounds as well as the sights of the pagentry. A party of dancing girls bearing the spoils of the conquered appears during the march, and at its conclusion, more soldiers enter, behind war chariots, flags and banners, sacred vessels and images of the dieties. The people and priests form a chorus to hail the victors and thank and praise their gods. At long last, Radames arrives, carried in under a canopy by twelve military officers.

Gloria all'Egitto, ad Iside
(Glory to Egypt, and to Isis)

PEOPLE

Gloria all'Egitto, ad Iside che il sacro suol protegge! Al re che il Delta regge inni festosi alziam! Gloria! Gloria! Gloria al re! Gloria! Inni alziam, *ecc.*	Glory to Egypt, and to Isis who protects its sacred soil! Let us raise festive hymns to the king who rules the Delta! Glory! Glory! Glory to the King! Glory! Let us raise hymns, *etc.*

WOMEN

S'intrecci il loto al lauro sul crin dei vincitori! Nembo gentil di fiori stenda sull'armi un vel. Danziam, fanciulle egizie, le mistiche carole, come d'intorno al sole danzano gli astri in ciel . . .	Let lotus be laced with laurel upon the heads of the conquerors! Let a sweet shower of flowers veil the arms of war. Let us dance, Egyptian maidens, the mystic dances, as the stars dance eternally around the sun in the sky . . .

Allegro maestoso

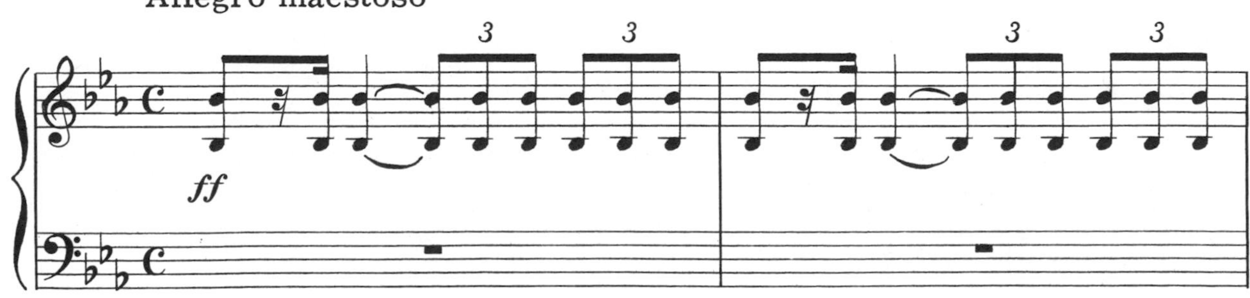

mf

CHORUS
ff a tempo come prima
Gloria all' E git - to, ad I - si - de che il sa-cro suol pro -
ff a tempo come prima
ff
teg - ge! Al Re che il Del - ta reg - ge, al
ff

Re che il Del - ta reg - ge in - ni fe - sto - si al-
pesanti

ziam! Glo - ria!
mf

Glo - ria!

Glo - ria!
Glo - ria al

Re! Glo - ria, glo - ria, glo - -
cresc. e stringendo a poco a poco

ria! In - ni al - ziam, in - ni al ziam! Glo -

ria
al
Re!
In - ni - fe -
f

cantabile
sto - si, fe - sto - si al - ziam!
S'in-

trec - ci il lo - to al lau - ro sul crin dei vin - ci -
p

to - ri! nem - bo gen - til di fio - ri

sten - da sull' ar mi un vel! Dan - ziam. fanciulle e-

gi - zie, le mi - sti - che ca - ro - le,

cresc.
co - me d'in-tor-no al so - le dan - za-no gli a - stri in
cresc.
ciel.
Triumphal March
3
mf
3
3
3
3

f
p
ff
mf

3
3
3
3

The King descends his throne to embrace the warrior, Egypt's gallant savior. Radames then kneels as Amneris offers him his crown of victory. When granted anything he might wish for his service to his country, he asks for the Ethiopian captives. Their entrance, surrounded by guards, here serves as a musical repose. A soldier in officer's dress is led in last. Aida, to her great surprise recognizing him as her father, embraces Amonasro, while he whispers that she must not give him away. Despite the hundreds of people on stage, Verdi here manages to center attention on this most intimate exchange.

When commanded to step forward and identify himself, Amonasro, pointing to his uniform, tells the King that he is an Ethiopian officer, a brave fighter for his country. He then begins his short but lovely plea for mercy, a plea echoed by the slaves and captives. At the same time, Ramphis and the priests urge the King to obey the decree of the gods and see that all Ethiopians are put to death.

Ma tu, re, tu signore possente

(But you, O King, you, O mighty lord)

AMONASRO

Ma tu, re, tu signore possente, a costoro ti volgi clemente. Oggi noi siam percossi dal fato, ah! doman voi potria il fato colpir.	But you, O King, you, O mighty lord, have mercy on these men. Today we are struck down by fate, but tomorrow fate may strike at you.

ten.
fa - to, ah! do - man voi po - tria il fa - to col - pir.
ten.
p

The scene continues with the various characters voicing individual thoughts. Radames, momentarily distracted by Aida's tearstained face, imagines that she is even more beautiful in her grief. Amneris, once again observing the looks of love and yearning that pass between Radames and her slave, privately renews her promise of revenge. Eventually, Radames steps forward to ask for mercy for the prisoners. He is certain Amonasro, the Ethiopian leader, is dead. Without him, the enemy is helpless. Ramphis disagrees, arguing that such mercy can only lead to more invasions, and feels that if this wish is granted, Amonasro should be kept as hostage to discourage further hostilities. The King prudently listens to both. He also presents Radames with the hand of his daughter in marriage, an award the hero cannot decline. As Amneris gloats, her pleasure fulfilled with this arranged bethrothal, Aida's thin hopes disappear altogether.

Act II ends with a huge chorus, all on stage voicing assorted sentiments. The King and his subjects extol the manifold virtues of their land, while Amonasro can already envision Ehiopia's reprisal. Predictably, Ramphis and the priests laud the gods, and the prisoners bless merciful Egypt's restoration of their freedom.

Unquestionably, Verdi's artistry served him well in this last scene of Act II. It is something of a small miracle that somehow, given such overwhelming circumstances, the intensely private emotions of the protagonists dominate the awesome, crowded, noisy pagentry, maintaining both interest in and involvement with the story. He again arranges to bring Aida's sufferings sharply into focus when the newly engaged couple take hands. There is much psychologically persuasive about the music as it reinforces the characteristic behavior of the priests and highlights the confident relish Ameris takes in her conquest of Aida's claims to Radames. The ballet material is distinctly oriental but separate from the sacred music in the same idiom and the characters are well differentiated in the final ensemble. It is no simple matter to keep a finale of these enormous proportions firmly in hand, but when meticulously directed, it is virtually unforgettable.

Act III

Act III

Characters in Order of Appearance: Ramphis and Amneris; Amonasro; Radames; Chorus of Priestesses [off stage].

Strings and harmonics on cello suggesting a hot, starry night open this act, and though the tension will mount without relief, the score retaining its power even when lyric and picturesque, Verdi continues throughout to illustrate the drama with expressively colored music.

It is the eve of the wedding of Amneris and Radames. A bright moon outlines a temple dedicated to Isis half-hidden by foliage on a rocky hill overlooking the Nile. Priestesses inside the temple are heard chanting to the goddess of love and law as a boat glides down the river and stops at the shrine. Ramphis and Amneris alight, in the company of heavily veiled women and guards. The pious chanting continues as Amneris, attended by Ramphis and the others, enters the temple where she must pass the hours before her marriage in prayer.

Also veiled and taking care not to be discovered, Aida now appears near the temple, her recitative explaining that she waits there for Radames. Bereft of hope, loveless, poignantly homesick, she here delivers an outstanding aria about her beloved Ethiopia, clarinets, bassoon and oboe helping her evoke vivid impressions of the natural splendors of a land she may never see again.

O patria mia
(O, my homeland)

AIDA

O patria mia, mai piu ti rivedro! . . . O cieli azzurri, o dolci aure native, dove sereno il mio mattin brillo; o verdi colli, o profumate rive, o patria mia, mai piu ti rivedro! O patria mia, mai piu, ah! mai piu ti rivedro! *ecc.* mai piu, no, no, mai piu! O fresche valli, o queto asil beato che un di promesso dall'amor mi fu! Or che d'amore il sogno e dileguato, o patria mia, non ti vedro mai piu! *ecc.* O patria mia, mai piu ti rivedro!	O, my homeland, I will never see you again! . . . O blue skies, O soft native breezes, where the light of my youth quietly sparkled; O, green hills, perfumed shores, O, my homeland, I will never see you again! O my homeland, never again, ah! I will never see you . . . *etc.* never again, never again! O, cool valleys, O, blessed, tranquil refuge which once was promised me by love! Now that the dream of love has faded, O, my homeland, I will never see you again! *etc.* O, my homeland, I will never see you again!

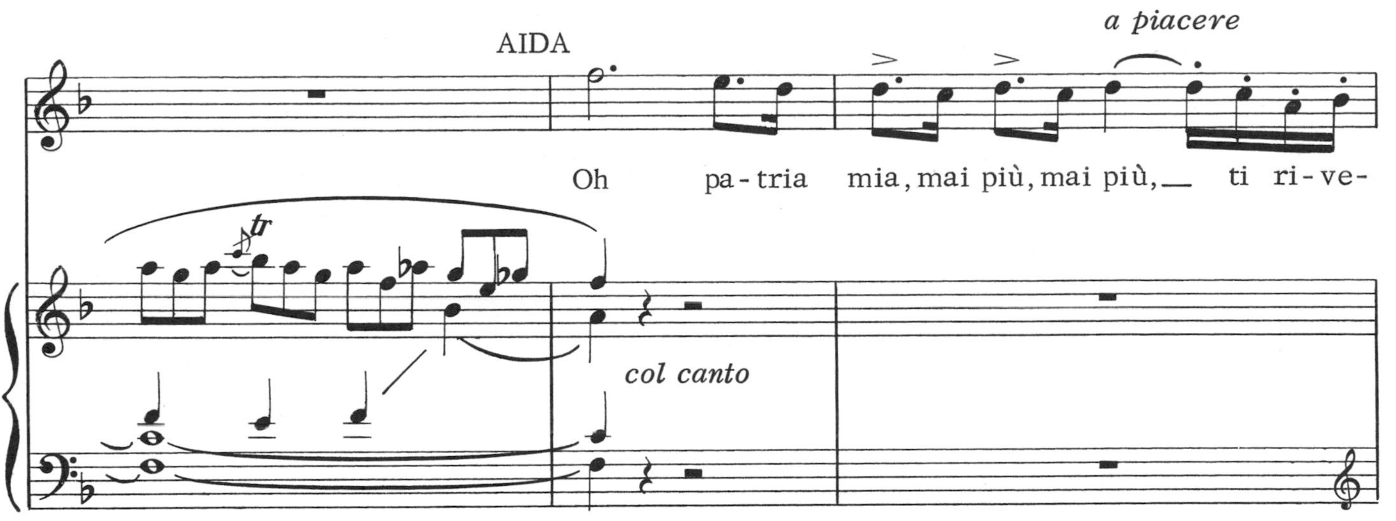
AIDA
a piacere
Oh pa-tria mia, mai più, mai più, ti ri-ve-
col canto

drò!
mai più!
p

mai più ti ri-ve-drò!
dim. dolcissimo

Lo stesso movimento
cantabile
O cieli az - zur-ri, o dol-ci au-re na-ti -

ve, do - ve se - re - no il mio mat-tin bril -

dolciss.
lo o ver - di col - li o pro - fu - ma - te

poco cresc.
ri - ve o pa - tria mi - a, mai più ti ri - ve-

lunga
drò! oh pa - tria
espress.
legato

mi - a, mai più, ah! mai
pp

Suddenly, Amonasro joins his nostalgic daughter, and begins this duet by assuring Aida that he understands her quandry, knows she loves Radames and that Amneris is her rival. But he has a solution for her. He too appreciates the peaceful beauty of Ethiopia and proposes that she and Radames take refuge there where they can be united in their love. He adds, however, one small condition. His troops have rearmed and stand ready for battle. Victory is certain if he can pinpoint the route Egyptian troops will be taking on their way to the fight. Radames knows this vital intelligence; he loves Aida and she has his confidence. Surely she can induce him to reveal it.

Rivedrai le foreste imbalsamate
(You shall see once more the perfumed forests)

AIDA

Rivedrai le foreste imbalsamate, le nostri valli, i nostri tempii d'or.	I shall see once more the perfumed forests . . .

AMONASRO

Sposa felice a lui che amasti tanto, tripudii immensi ivi potrai gioir.	Happy wife to him you love so much, there you will be able to enjoy untold happiness . . .

AIDA

Un giorno solo di si dolce incanto, un'ora, un'ora di tal gioia, e poi morir!	One single day of such sweet enchantment, one hour, one hour of such a joy, and then to die!

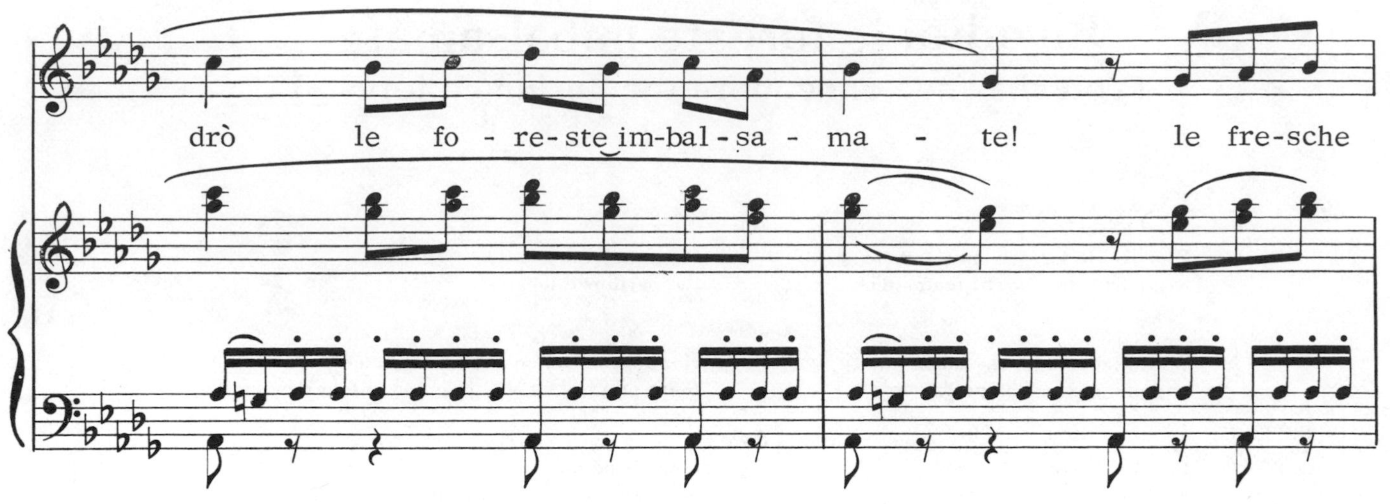
drò le fo-re-ste im-bal-sa-ma - te! le fre-sche

AMONASRO
val - li, i no-stri tem-pli d'òr! Spo-sa fe -

li - ce a lui che a-ma-sti tan - to, tri-pu-dii im-

AIDA
men - si i - vi po - trai gio - ir Un gior-no
col canto

so - lo di si dol-ce in - can - to u-n' o ra, u-
cresc.

n'o - ra di tal gio-ia, e poi mo-rir! e poi mo - rir!
tr

Aida, horrified by his suggestion, refuses to enter into any such conspiracy, thereby unleasing Amonasro's most primitive fury. He denounces her, utterly, while frenzied strings and brasses underscore the blood bathed defeat and disgrace her refusal will surely bring to her homeland. He will not hear her pleadings; but continues to abuse her, even as she begs at his feet for charity. Once the daughter of a king, she is now, in his pitiless eyes, forever condemned to remain a mere slave of the Egyptians. The duet ends when Amonasro, hearing Radames approach, quickly moves to hide among some palms nearby.

Pensa che un popolo
(Remember that a people can rise)

AMONASRO

Pensa che un popolo, vinto, straziato, per te soltanto risorger puo.	Remember that a people, conquered and tormented, can rise again because of you.

AIDA

O patria! O patria, quanto mi costi!	O my country, what you have cost me!

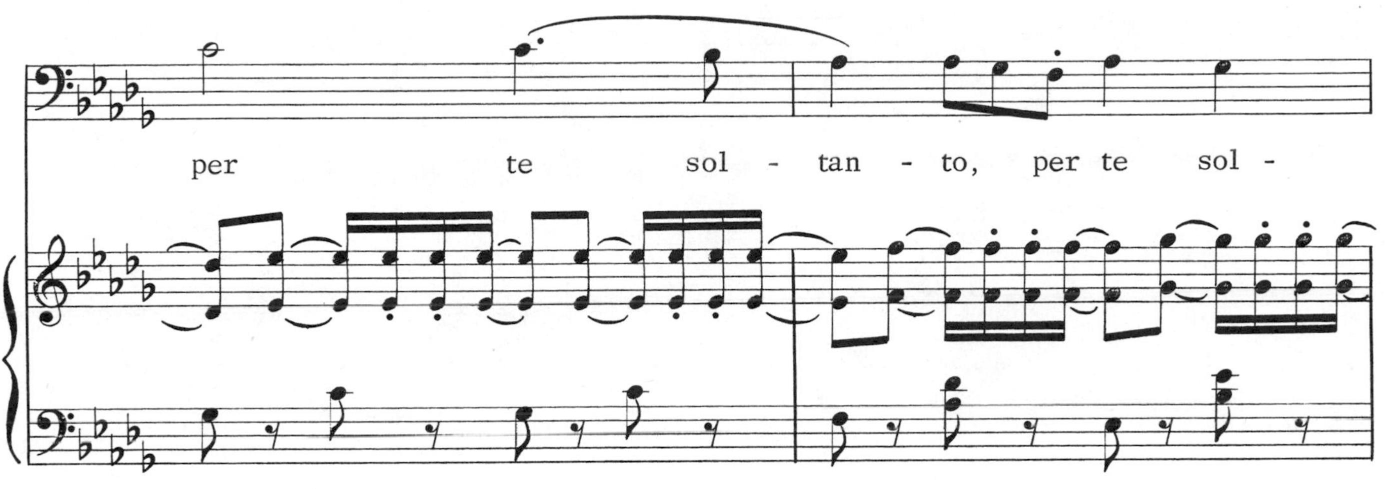
per te sol - tan - to, per te sol -

AIDA
tan - to ri - sor - ger può. Oh pa - tria! oh
cresc. poco a poco

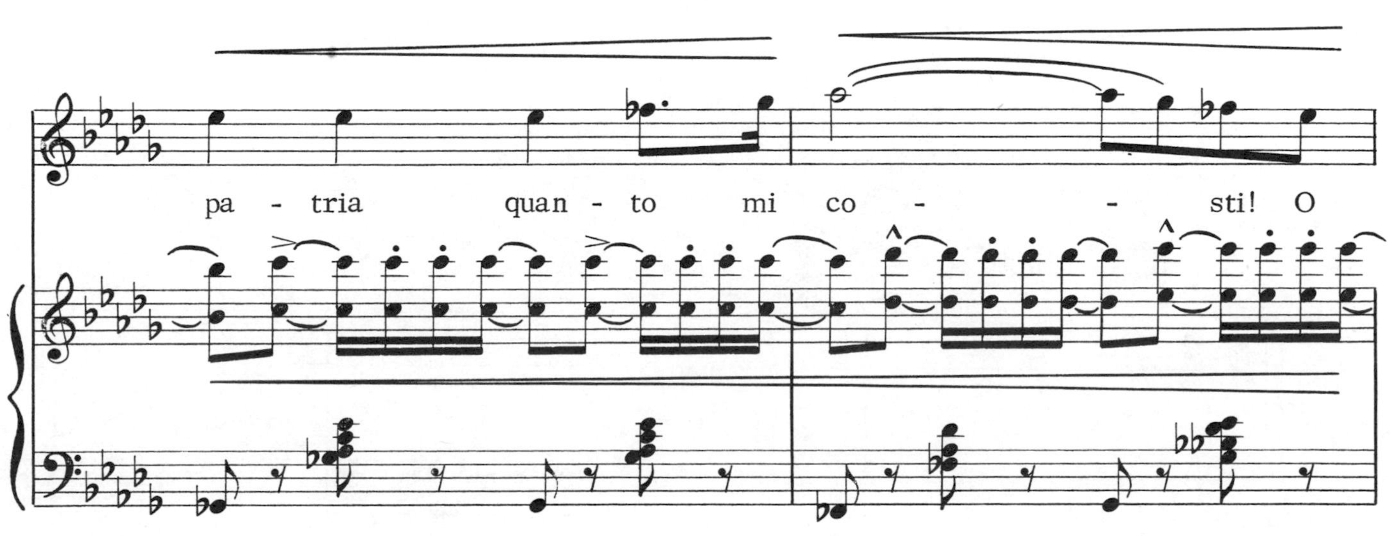
pa - tria quan - to mi co - - sti! O

In the passage that follows his quite conventional entrance, Radames tells Aida of his great joy at seeing her.

Purti riveggo
(Once more I see you)

Radames

Pur ti riveggo, mia dolce Aida.	Once more I see you, my sweet Aida.

Aida

T'arresta. Vanne. Che speri ancor?	Stop. Go away. What can you yet hope for?

Radames

A te dappresso l'amore mi guida.	Love leads me to you.

Aida

Te i riti attendono d'un altro amor. D'Amneris sposo . . .	The rites of another love await you. Husband of Amneris . . .

Radames

Che parli mai? Te sola, Aida, te deggio amar. Gli dei m'ascoltano, tu mia sarai.	What are you saying? I must love only you, Aida. The gods hear me; you shall be mine.

Allegro giusto

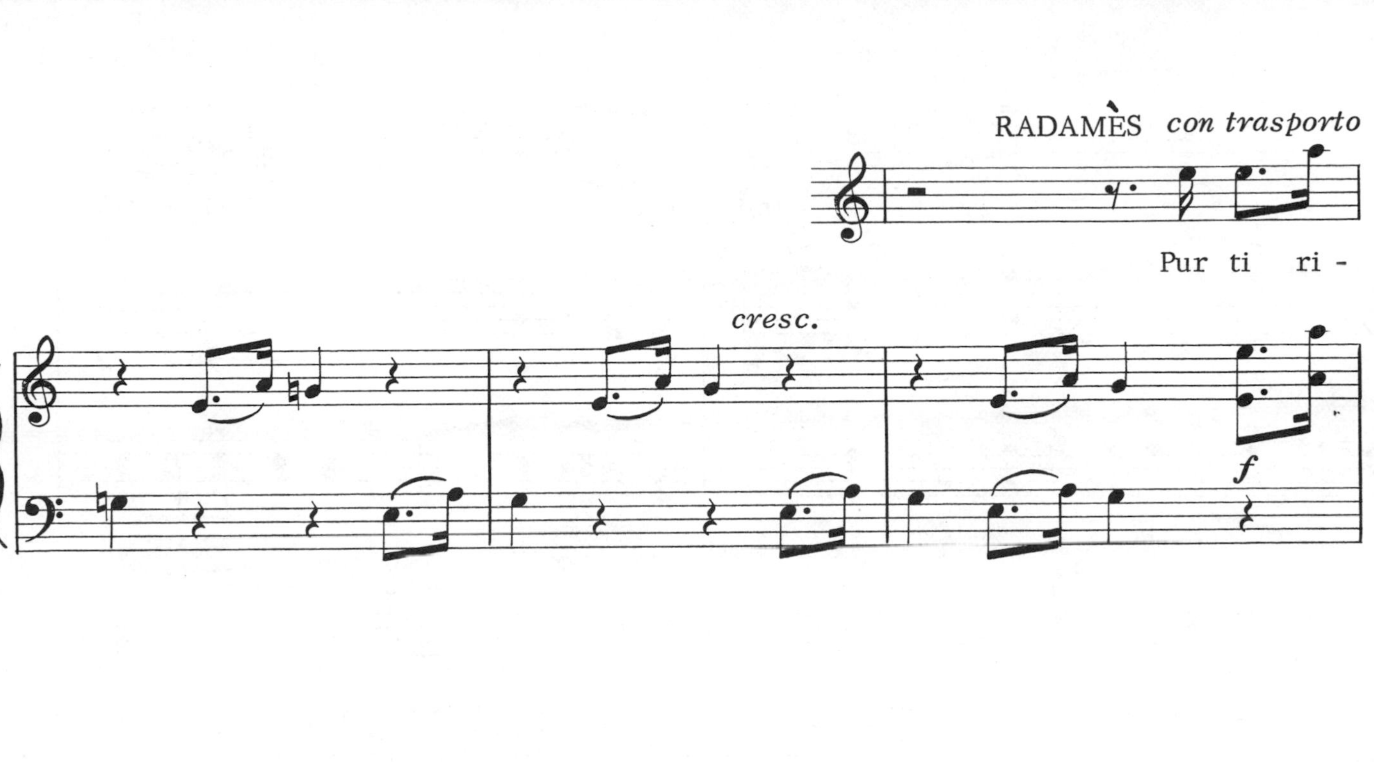
RADAMÈS con trasporto
Pur ti ri-
cresc.
f

AIDA
veg - go, mia dol-ce A - i - da T'ar-res - ta,

RADAMÈS
van - ne che spe - ri an - cor? A te dap-

AIDA
pres - so l'a-mor mi gui - da. Te i ri - ti at-
marc.
ten - do-no d'un al - tro a-mor. D'Am-ne - ris
RADAMÈS
accel.
spo - so. Che par - li mai? Te so - la, A-
al tempo
i - da, te deg - gio a - mar. Gli Dei m'a-
f
al tempo

scol - ta-no tu mia sa - ra - i
etc.

But he cannot console her with his foolish insistence that everything will be all right. Aida, well aware that none can defy royal commands, the gods or the will of the people, knows Amneris will see them both destroyed if they stay. There is no choice but to run far from Egypt, and the musical painting of her "La tra foreste vergine" section in effect seduces Radames with promises of a paradise deep in the forest where their love can flourish.

La, tra foreste vergini,
(There, in virgin forests)

AIDA

La, tra foreste vergini, di fiori profumate, in estasi beate la terra scorderem, in estasi la terra scorderem.	There, in virgin forests, perfumed with flowers, in beautiful ecstasy we shall forget the world, in ecstasy we shall forget the world.

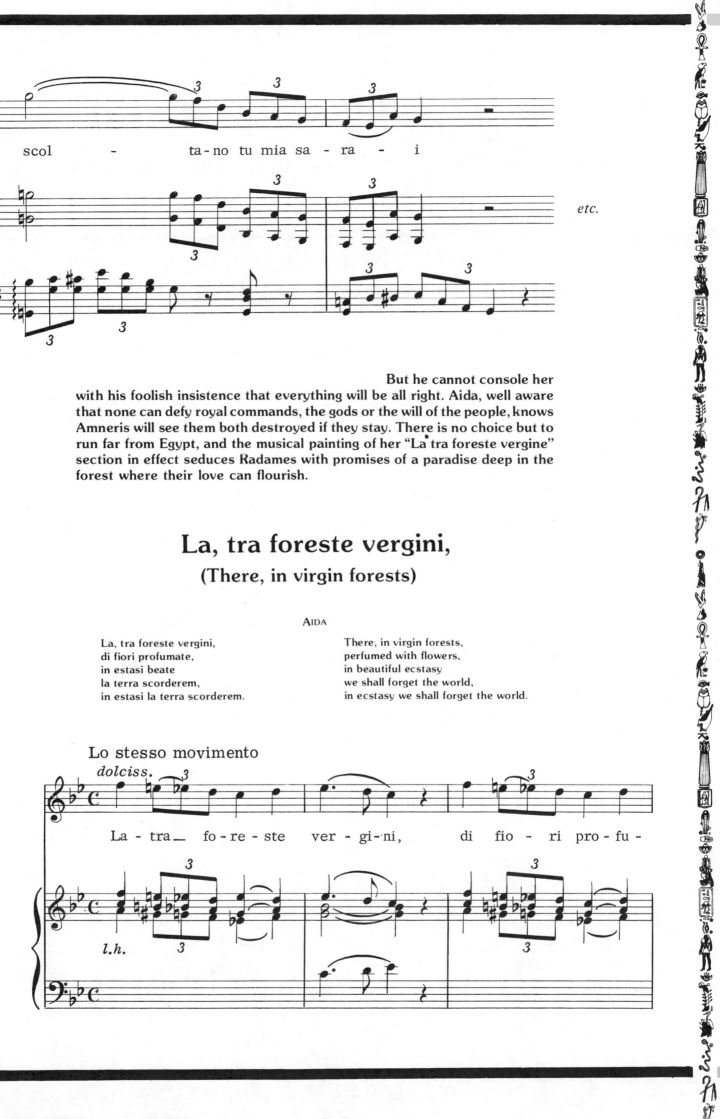

Lo stesso movimento
dolciss.
La - tra fo-re-ste ver - gi-ni, di fio - ri pro-fu -
l.h.

estremamente p
ma - te, in e - sta si be - a - te la
estremamente p
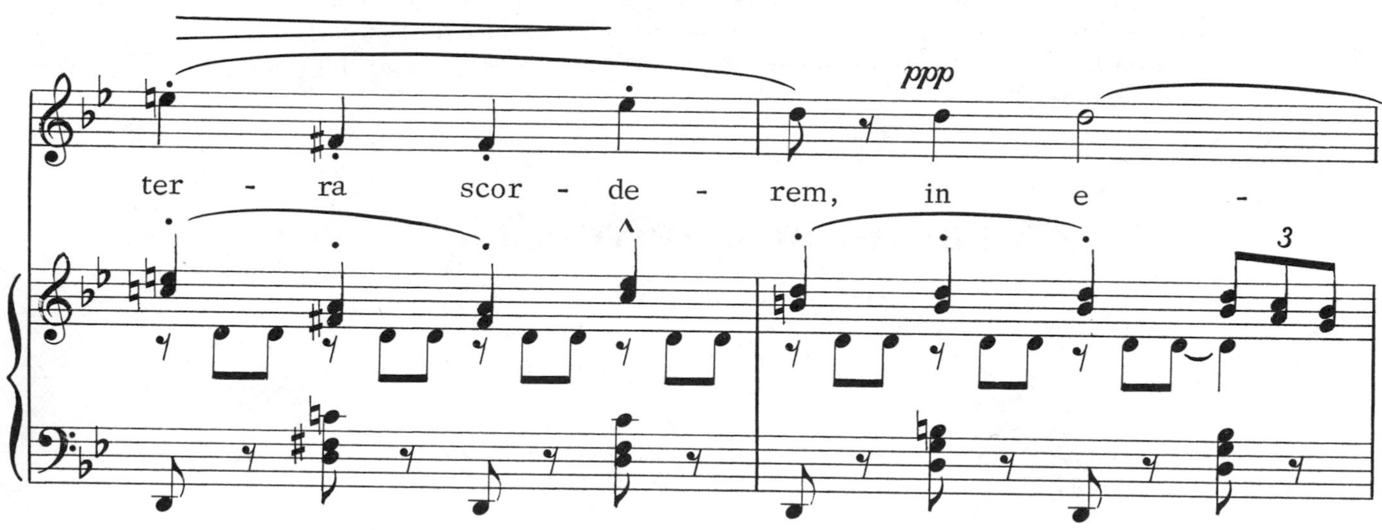
ppp
ter - ra scor - de - rem, in e -

- sta - si, in e -

He hesitates. It is treason to flee. But when at last he agrees, they finish their duet together resolved to find that paradise far from all sorrow and imprisonment.

Ah no! Fuggiamo!
(Ah no! Let us flee!)

RADAMES

Ah no! Fuggiamo! Si: fuggiam da queste mura, al deserto insiem fuggiamo; qui sol regna la sventura, la si schiude un ciel d'amor. I deserti interminati a noi talamo saranno, su noi gli astri brilleranno di piu limpido fulgor.	Ah no! Let us flee! Yes: let us flee from these walls, let us flee, together to the desert; here, nothing but misfortune reigns, there a paradise of love awaits us. The endless desert will be our bridal bed, and the stars will shine above us with a brighter light.

AIDA

Nella terra avventurata de' miei padri, il ciel ne attende; ivi l'aura e imbalsamata, ivi il suolo e aromi e fior. Fresche valli e verdi prati a noi talamo saranno, su noi gli astri brilleranno di piu limpido fulgor.	Heaven awaits us in my ancestors' blessed country; the breeze is sweetly perfumed there, the soil is fragrant with flowers there. Cool valleys and green meadows will be our bridal bed, and the stars will shine above us with a brighter light.

AIDA *and* RADAMES

Vieni meco, insiem fuggiamo questa terra di dolor. Vieni meco, t'amo, t'amo! A noi duce fia l'amore.	Come with me, together let us flee this land of sorrow. Come with me, I love you, I love you! Love will be our guide.

Allegro assai vivo
RADAMÈS
Si: fug - giam da que - ste mu - ra, al_ de -
p cresc.
ppp
pp
ser - to in - siem fug - gia - mo; qui sol re - gna la sven -
p
tu - ra, là_ si_ schiu - de un ciel d'a - mor. I de -
pp
ser - ti in - ter - mi - na - ti a noi_ ta - la - mo_ sa -

ran - no, su noi gli a - stri bril - le - ran - no di più
col canto

in tempo
AIDA
lim - pi - do ful - gor. Nel - la ter - ra av - ven - tu-
in tempo
p cresc.

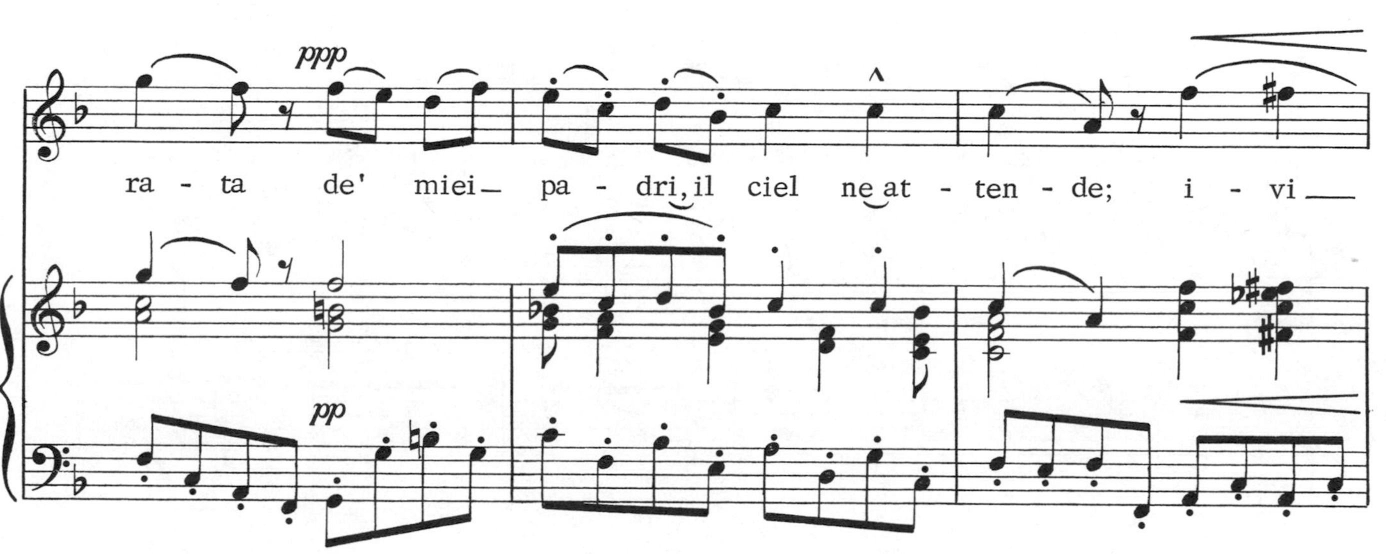
ppp
ra - ta de' miei pa - dri, il ciel ne at - ten - de; i - vi
pp

pp
l'au-ra è im-bal - sa-ma - ta, i vi il suolo è a-ro - mi e
pp

fior. Fre - sche val - li e ver-di pra - ti a noi

ta la-mo sa-ran - no, su noi gli a-stri bril - le -

molto riten.
ran - no di più lim - pi - do ful - gor. Vie-ni
col canto
f
molto riten.

(molto riten.)
me - - co, in-siem fug - gia - mo que - sta
(molto riten.)

ter - ra di do - lor, Vie - ni

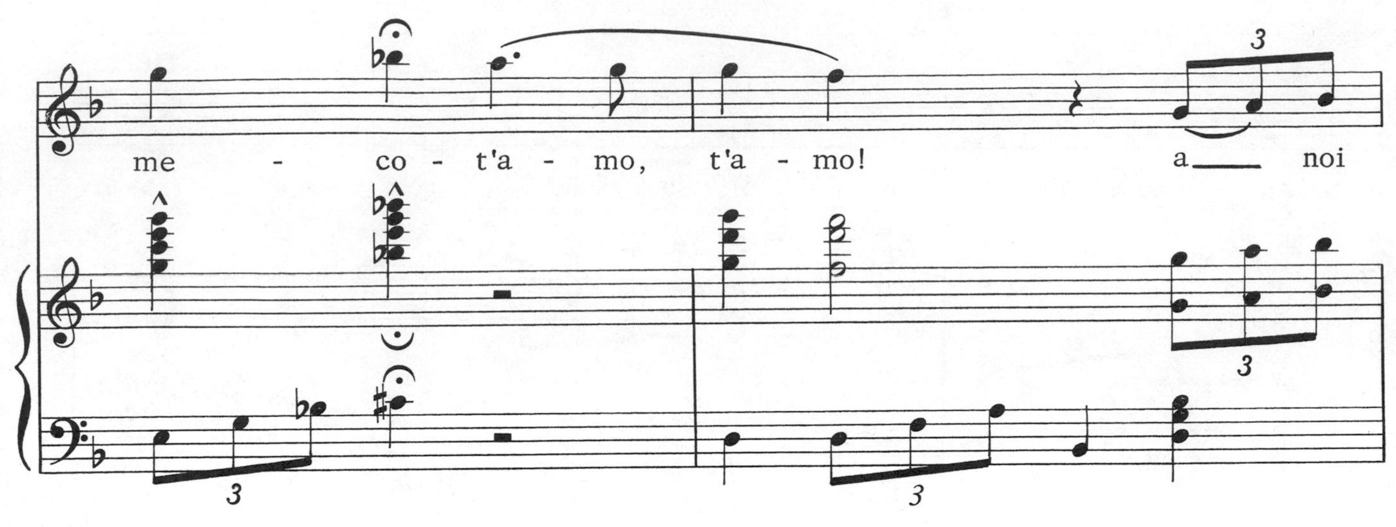
me - co - t'a - mo, t'a - mo! a noi

du - ce fia l'a - mor, fia l'a - mor.
etc.

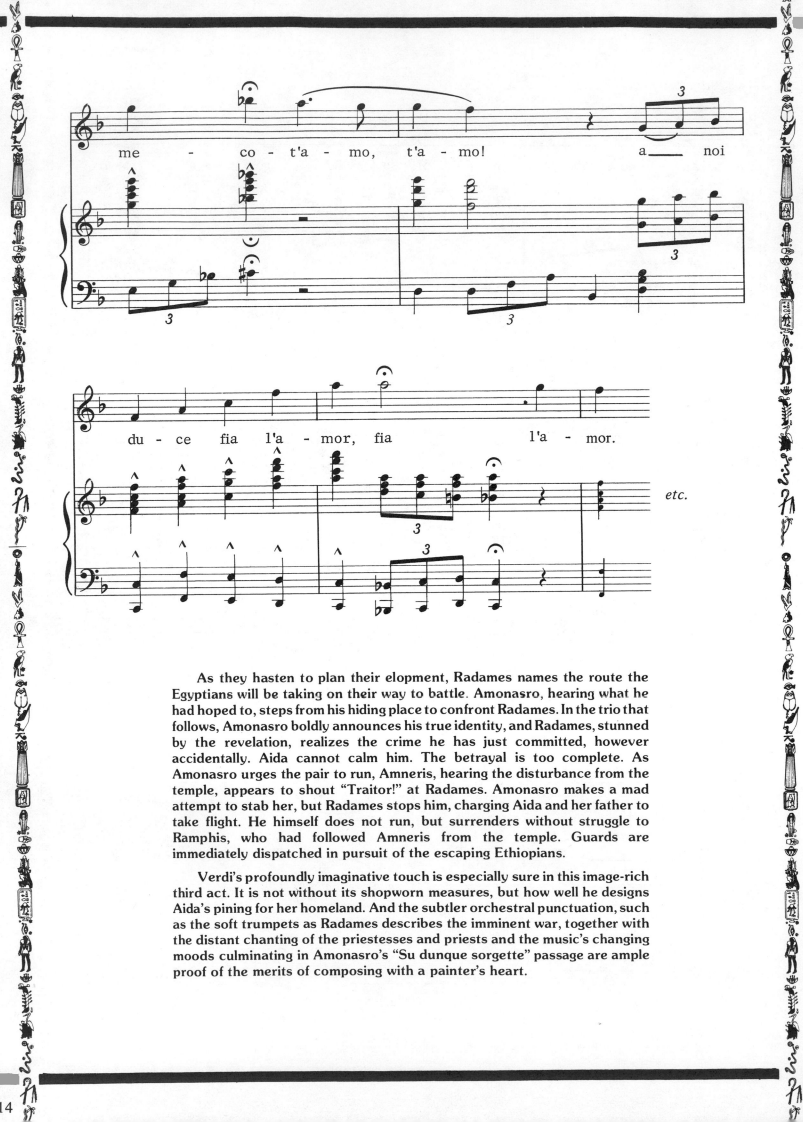

As they hasten to plan their elopment, Radames names the route the Egyptians will be taking on their way to battle. Amonasro, hearing what he had hoped to, steps from his hiding place to confront Radames. In the trio that follows, Amonasro boldly announces his true identity, and Radames, stunned by the revelation, realizes the crime he has just committed, however accidentally. Aida cannot calm him. The betrayal is too complete. As Amonasro urges the pair to run, Amneris, hearing the disturbance from the temple, appears to shout "Traitor!" at Radames. Amonasro makes a mad attempt to stab her, but Radames stops him, charging Aida and her father to take flight. He himself does not run, but surrenders without struggle to Ramphis, who had followed Amneris from the temple. Guards are immediately dispatched in pursuit of the escaping Ethiopians.

Verdi's profoundly imaginative touch is especially sure in this image-rich third act. It is not without its shopworn measures, but how well he designs Aida's pining for her homeland. And the subtler orchestral punctuation, such as the soft trumpets as Radames describes the imminent war, together with the distant chanting of the priestesses and priests and the music's changing moods culminating in Amonasro's "Su dunque sorgette" passage are ample proof of the merits of composing with a painter's heart.

Act IV

Act IV

Scene I

Characters in Order of Appearance: Amneris; Radames; Ramphis and Priests.

The first portion of the final act is entirely dominated by Amneris, the ingeniously flexible music exploiting the full range of her exhausting emotional agonies, one after another, as she waits for, then decries, the judgment of Radames. Both themes associated with her in Act I are present, but the score blends this subjective emotionalism with more objective theatricalism, apparent in the familiar chanting of the priests and the frequently narrative orchestration.

As the scene opens on a hall in the Pharoh's palace, Amneris is found crouched at the entrance portal leading to underground courtrooms where the priests have gathered. A passageway on the right leads to the prison where Radames is being held awaiting trial. In a short recitative, she tells of Aida's disappearance, and though the priests are meeting to decide the fate of Radames, the princess laments that she is cursed to love him yet, despite his betrayal.

Io l'amo
(I love him)

AMNERIS

Io l'amo, io l'amo sempre . . .	I love him, I will always love him . . .
Disperato, insano e quest'amor	This love which is destroying
che la mia vita strugge.	my life is hopeless, insane.
O! s'ei potesse amarmi!	Oh, if he could love me!

sem - pre Di-spe-ra - to, in - sa - so è que-st'a -
mor che la mia vi - ta strug - ge.
Oh! s'ei po - tes - se a - mar - mi!
etc.

By now convinced of his innocence, Amneris, deciding to offer him one last chance for salvation, orders the guards to bring the prisoner to her. When Radames is led in, she begins their duet with a passage, full of foreboding, describing his vulnerable position. But he will have no part of her offer to plead for him at her father's throne. If his intentions were harmless, he nevertheless did reveal a military secret and has the honor to pay for it. The music changes as Amneris continues, all her reserves breaking down, to beg him to reconsider.

Ah! tu dei vivere!
(Ah, you must live!)

AMNERIS

Morire!	To die!
Ah! tu dei vivere!	Ah, you must live!
Si, all'amor mio vivrai;	Yes, you shall live for my love;
per te le angoscie orribili	I have already endured
di morte io gia provai;	the terrible anguish of death.
t'amai . . . soffersi tanto . . .	I loved you . . . I suffered so much . . .
vegliai le notti in pianto . . .	I lay awake at night in tears . . .
e patria, e trono, e vita	and country, throne and life,
tutto darei, tutto, tutto, darei per te.	everything, everything I would give up for you.

te le an-go - scie or-ri - bi-li di mor - te io già pro-
ppp
legato
accentate
va-i; t'a- mai, sof-fer - si tan - to ve-
dolciss.
grandioso
glia - i le not-ti fa pian - to e pa - tria, e
fz
f

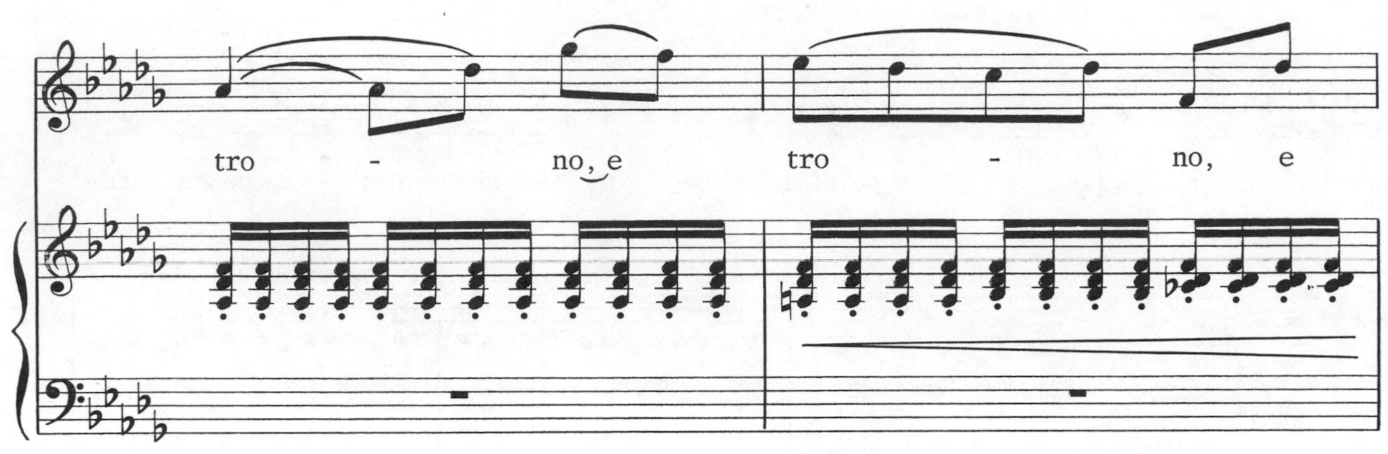
tro - no, e tro - no, e

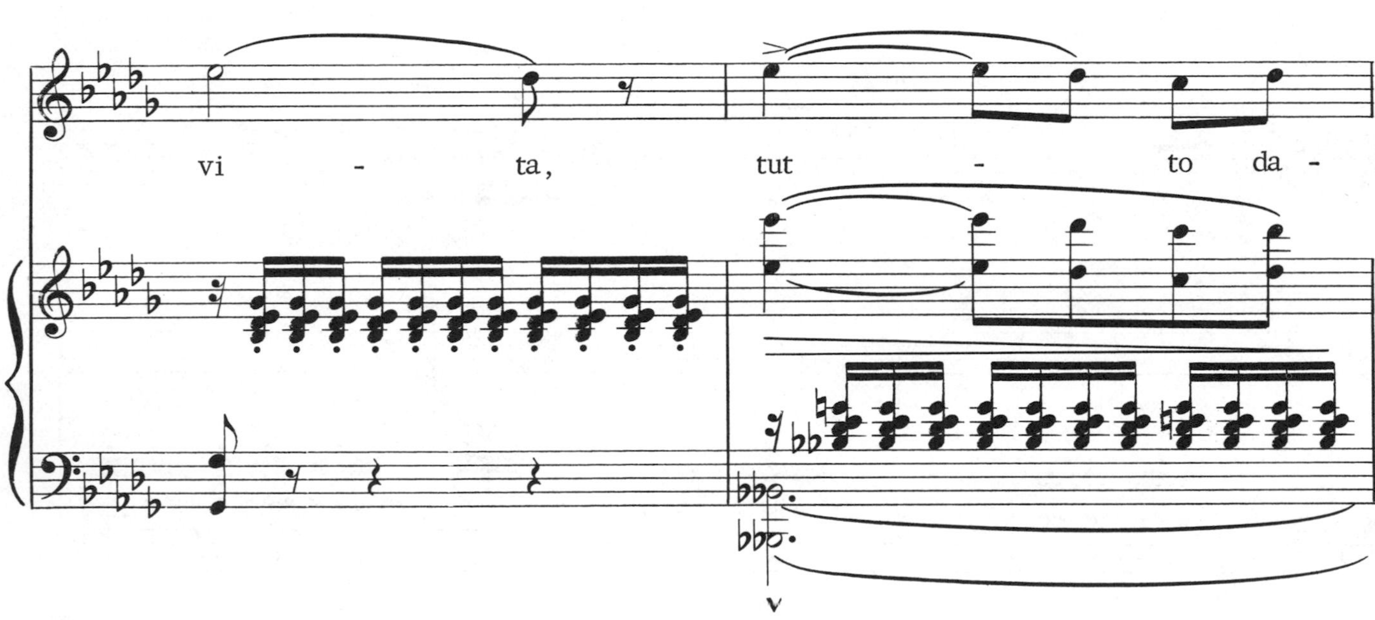
vi - ta, tut - to da -

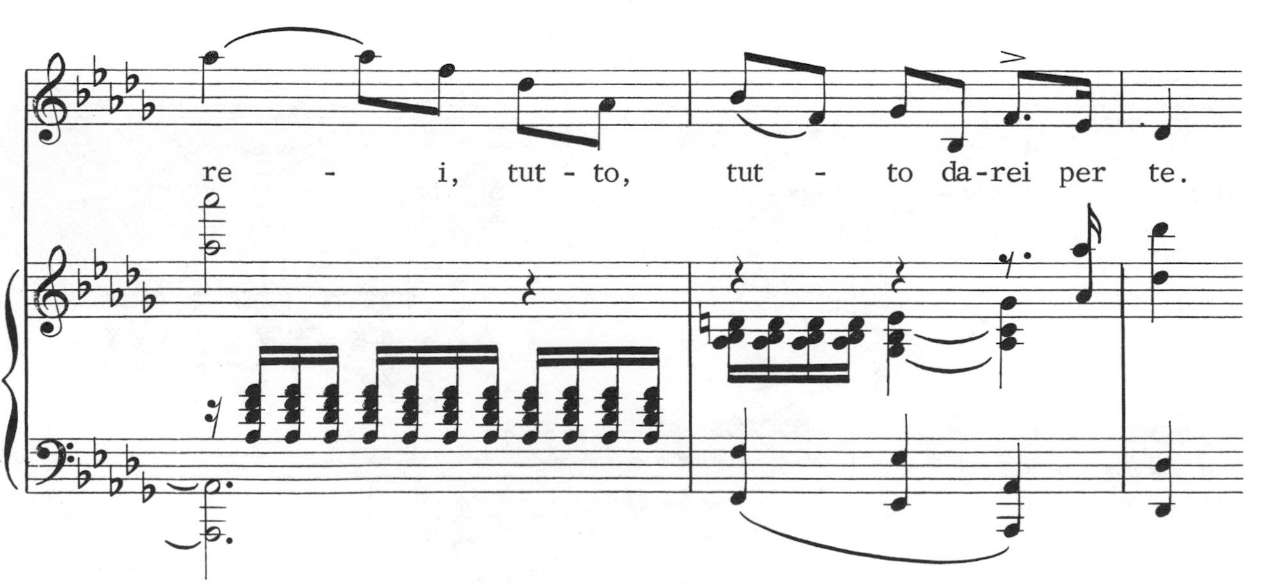
re - i, tut-to, tut - to da-rei per te.

Answering only that he has nothing to live for now that Aida is gone, Radames believes that Amneris has murdered Aida with her malevolent spite. He can hardly give his life to such a coldblooded executioner. Amneris denies the accusation, insisting that though Amonasro is known dead, Aida still lives. He has only to swear never to see her again to be spared. Radames, fully prepared to die, refuses. On this refusal, Amneris, far beyond all reason, promises the soldier that his death will requite the countless tears she has wasted on him. After he is led away, asking to be spared both her anger and her pity, Amneris, overcome, collapses.

Most of the material in this duet, following Radames's entrance, is new. The gradual working up of its intensity is tempered by a passage of compelling beauty when Radames prays for Aida's safe escape to Ethiopia. The excitement of the account of the flight of Aida and Amonasro culminates in the black despair of Amneris as Radames resolves to die. The scene of trial and condemnation continues emotionally charged.

Amneris, once again alone, fast regrets her storming outburst. Must she not now blame herself for her lover's disgrace? As she sings of her remorse, priests cross the hall and enter the court, and she closes her repentences, despondent, burying her face in her hands.

The judgment sequence begins as Ramphis leads a chorus in a brief unaccompanied invocation to the gods. Watching the guards escort Radames to the courtroom, knowing he is now beyond her influence, Amneris cries out "Oh! chi lo salva?" (Oh! who can save him?). The priests formally charge the accused with treason; three times the accusation and demands for explanation are repeated, each charge followed by soft drumming, and three times Radames is silent. The silence taken as an admission of guilt, the death warrant specifies that he suffer burial alive. On hearing the verdict, Amneris, having grown increasingly hysterical as the trial progressed, climaxes the scene with a wild denunciation of the priests. They choose to ignore her, filing offstage, leaving her to exit spent and distraught.

Act IV

Scene II

Characters in Order of Appearance: Radames; Aida; Priests and Priestesses; Amneris.

The last scene of the opera, in sharp contrast to the one preceding it, is neither dramatic nor conventionally emotional. Verdi was a mature composer when he accepted the commission to write *Aida*; his practiced instincts told him that after all the turbulence, pain and passion, this work's final statement must be like its beginning, uncommonly quiet, lyrical, almost comforting.

By dividing the set into two floors, the upper representing the magnificent gold-glittering interior of the Temple of Vulcan, the lower the dark, shadowy crypt, the death sequence is realized not only by the victims, but by the survivors as well. Radames is already installed in his tomb when it begins, and as two priests above adjust the stone that closes the grave forever, he comes to terms with his fate, hoping only that Aida will live happily, never learning of his end. But his philosophic musings, interrupted when he hears someone sobbing close by, turn to horror when he recognizes Aida hidden there among the shadows, waiting to die beside him. At the thought of her dying that way, even if he can calmly face his own sentence, he frantically tries to dislodge the stone sealing their doom. In the temple above, the priests and priestesses have again begun the slow chant of their prayers. And below, when his desperate strength yields nothing, Radames sadly cedes to death's ordained victory.

Morir! si pura e bella!

To die! So pure and lovely!

RADAMES

Morir! si pura el bella!	To die! So pure and lovely!
morir per me d'amore;	To die for love of me;
degli anni tuoi nel fiore	to flee from life
fuggir la vita!	in the flower of your youth!
T'avea il cielo per l'amor creata,	Heaven created you for love,
ed io t'uccido per averti amata!	and I am killing you by loving you!
No, non morrai!	No, you shall not die!
troppo t'amai!	I have loved you too much!
troppo sei bella!	You are too beautiful!

rir! per me d'a-mo - re de - gli an - ni tuoi nel

dolciss. senza string.
fio - re, de-gl'an-ni tuoi nel fio - re fug-gir la vi - -

ta! T'a-vea il cie-lo per l'a-mor cre - a - ta, ed io tuc-

con espressione
ci - do per a - ver - ti a - ma - ta! No, non mor -

dim. con grazia dolciss. e legato
rai! trop-po t'a-mai! trop-po sei bel - là!
tr

AIDA

Vedi? di morte l'angelo	Do you see? The radiant angel of
radiante a noi s'appressa,	death hastens toward us,
ne adduce a eterni gaudii	and carries us to eternal joy
sovra i suoi vanni d'or.	upon his golden wings.
Gia veggo il ciel dischiudersi . . .	I already see heaven opening . . .
ivi ogni affanno cessa . . .	there, all sorrow ceases . . .
ivi comincia l'estasi	there, begins the ecstasy
d'un immortale amor.	of an immortal love.

Andantino
AIDA dolciss.
Ve - di? di mor-te l'an-ge-lo ra-dian-te a noi s'ap-

pres - sa
ne ad - du - ce a e - ter - ni gau - dii
tr
sov - ra i suoi van - ni d'or.
Già veg - go il ciel di -
ppp
dolce
dim.
schiu - der si i vi o - gni af - fan - no ces - sa,

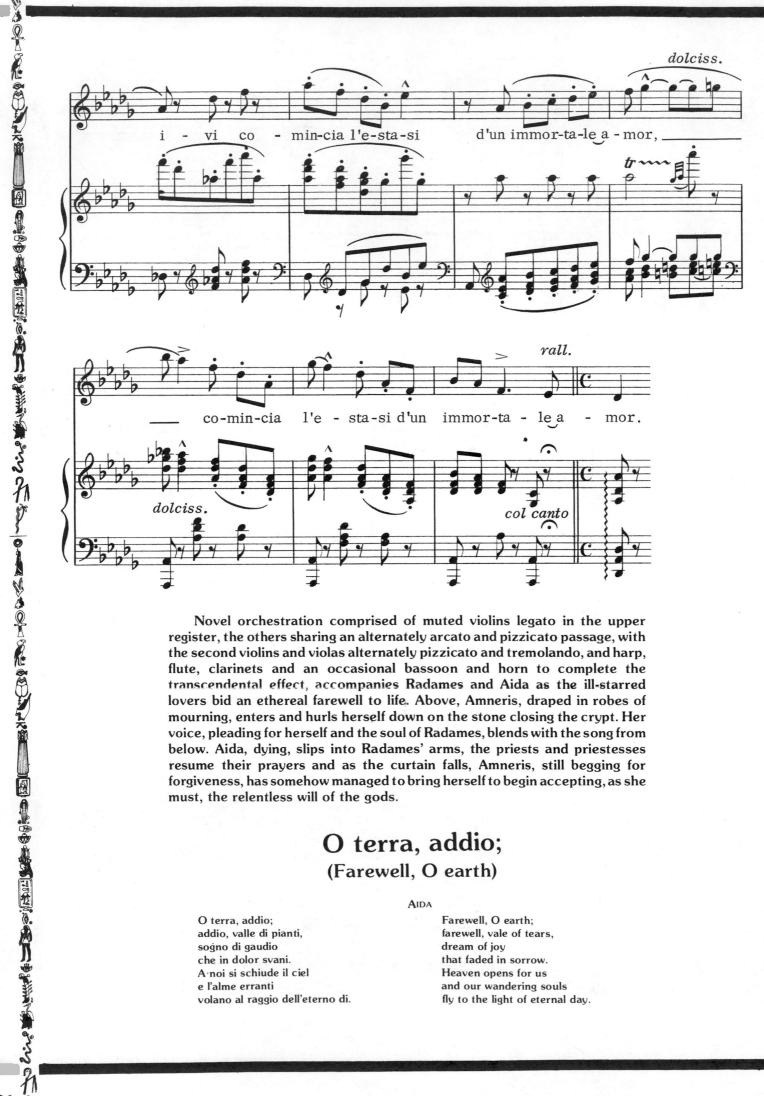

Novel orchestration comprised of muted violins legato in the upper register, the others sharing an alternately arcato and pizzicato passage, with the second violins and violas alternately pizzicato and tremolando, and harp, flute, clarinets and an occasional bassoon and horn to complete the transcendental effect, accompanies Radames and Aida as the ill-starred lovers bid an ethereal farewell to life. Above, Amneris, draped in robes of mourning, enters and hurls herself down on the stone closing the crypt. Her voice, pleading for herself and the soul of Radames, blends with the song from below. Aida, dying, slips into Radames' arms, the priests and priestesses resume their prayers and as the curtain falls, Amneris, still begging for forgiveness, has somehow managed to bring herself to begin accepting, as she must, the relentless will of the gods.

O terra, addio;

(Farewell, O earth)

AIDA

O terra, addio;	Farewell, O earth;
addio, valle di pianti,	farewell, vale of tears,
sogno di gaudio	dream of joy
che in dolor svani.	that faded in sorrow.
A noi si schiude il ciel	Heaven opens for us
e l'alme erranti	and our wandering souls
volano al raggio dell'eterno di.	fly to the light of eternal day.

Meno mosso
AIDA
O ter-ra ad-di-o; ad-di-o val-le di
ppp
f ten.
pp
pian-ti, so-gno di gau-dio che in do-lor sva-ni A noi si
schiu-de, si schiu-de il ciel, si schiu-de il ciel e l'al-me er-ran-
f
ti vo-la-no al rag-gio dell' e-ter-no dì.
dolciss.

METROPOLITAN OPERA

Tuesday Evening, February 3, 1976, 8:00-11:30

A Benefit for the Metropolitan Opera Production Funds, sponsored by the Metropolitan Opera Guild

PREMIERE

NEW PRODUCTION

The 579th Metropolitan Opera performance of

GIUSEPPE VERDI

Aida

Opera in four acts

Libretto by Antonio Ghislanzoni

Conductor:	James Levine
Production:	John Dexter
Set Designer:	David Reppa
Costume Designer:	Peter J. Hall
Lighting Designer:	Gilbert Hemsley (Debut)

Characters in order of vocal appearance:

Ramfis	Bonaldo Giaiotti
Radames	James McCracken
Amneris	Marilyn Horne
Aida	Leontyne Price
The King	James Morris
A messenger	Charles Anthony
A priestess	Marcia Baldwin
Amonasro	Cornell MacNeil

Choreographer:	Louis Johnson
Dancers:	
Act I, Scene 2:	Jack Hertzog
Act II, Scene 1:	Eleanor Bobb, Nicolyn Emanuel, Diana Levy
Act II, Scene 2:	William Badolato, Stanley Perryman (Debut) and Corps de Ballet
Chorus Master:	David Stivender
Musical Preparation:	Alberta Masiello
Assistant Stage Directors:	Bruce Donnell and David Sell
Special guest supernumerary:	Jim Dolan

This production of *Aida* was made possible by a generous and deeply appreciated gift from the Gramma Fisher Foundation, Marshalltown, Iowa.

Latecomers will not be admitted during the performance. *Knabe Piano used exclusively.*

The photographs on the following pages are from the new production of "Aida" by the Metropolitan Opera. They are: Act I, Scene 1—page 129; Act I, Scene 2—page 130; Act II, Scene 2—pages 131 and 132; Act III—pages 133 and 134; Act IV, Scene 1—page 135; Act IV, Scene 2—page 136. Photographs: The Metropolitan Opera Guild/Frank Dunand.

The Libretto

ACT I

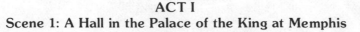

Scene 1: A Hall in the Palace of the King at Memphis

(Radames and Ramfis in consultation)

RAMFIS

Si: corre voce che l'Etiope ardisca
sfidarci ancora, e del Nilo la valle
e Tebe minacciar. Fra breve un messo
rechera il ver.

Yes, rumor has it that Ethiopia will dare
to defy us again and threaten the Nile
Valley and also Thebes. Shortly, a messenger
will bring us the truth.

RADAMES

La sacra Iside consultasti?

Have you consulted the will of Isis?

RAMFIS

Ella ha nomato dell'egizie falangi
il condottier supremo.

She has named the commander
of the Egyptian armies.

RADAMES

O lui felice!

O happy man!

RAMFIS

Giovane e prode è desso.

He is young and valiant.

(as he departs)

Ora, del nume
reco i decreti al re.

I now bear the divine
orders for the King.

RADAMES

Se quel guerrier io fossi!
Se il mio sogno si avverasse!
Un esercito di prodi da me guidato,
e la vittoria, e il plauso
di Menfi tutta!
E a te, mia dolce Aida,
tornar di lauri cinto . . .
dirti: per te ho pugnato,
per te ho vinto!

If only I were that warrior!
If only my dreams would come true!
A valiant army led by me,
and victory and the praise
of all Memphis!
And to return to you, my sweet
Aida, crowned with laurels . . .
to tell you: for you I fought,
for you I conquered!

Celeste Aida, forma divina,
mistico serto di luce e fior,
del mio pensiero tu sei regina,
tu di mia vita sei lo splendor.
Il tuo bel cielo vorrei ridarti,
le dolci brezze del patrio suol . . .
un regal serto sul crin posarti,
ergerti un trono vicino al sol. Ah!
Celeste Aida, forma divina,
mistico raggio di luce e fior, *ecc.*

Heavenly Aida, divine form,
mystical garland of light and flowers,
you are the queen of my thoughts,
you are the light of my life.
I would return you your lovely sky,
the gentle breezes of your native land . . .
I would set a royal crown upon your head
and build you a throne next the sun. Ah!
Heavenly Aida, form divine,
mystical ray of light and flowers, *etc.*

AMNERIS

(who has entered and stands observing Radames)

Quale insolita gioia
nel tuo sguardo!
Di quale nobil fierezza
ti balena il volto!
Degna d'invidia, o! quanto
saria la donna
il cui bramato aspetto
tanta luce di gaudio
in te destasse!

What unusual joy
gleams in your gaze!
What noble courage
glows in your face!
Oh, how envied
is that woman
whose unforseen image
could awaken in you
such a flame of rapture!

	RADAMES
D'un sogno avventuroso si beava il mio cuore. Oggi la diva profferse il nome del guerrier che al campo le schiere egizie condurrà. Ah, s'io fossi a tal onor prescelto.	My heart was rapturing in an adventurous dream. Today the goddess has announced the name of the warrior who will lead the Egyptian armies in the field. Ah, if I were chosen for such an honor!
	AMNERIS
Nè un altro sogno mai piu gentil, più soave, al core ti parlò? Non hai tu in Menfi desiderii, speranze?	Has no other dream, more gentle, more sweet, spoken to your heart? Here in Memphis have you no desires, no hopes?
	RADAMES
Io?	I?
	(to himself)
Quale inchiesta! Forse l'arcano amore scopri che m'arde in core.	Such a question! Perhaps she has discovered the secret love that burns in my heart.
	AMNERIS
	(to herself)
O'guai, se un altro amore ardesse a lui nel core!	Oh, woe, if another love should burn within his heart!
	RADAMES
Della sua schiava il nome mi lesse nel pensier!	She has read the name of her slave in my thoughts!
	AMNERIS
Guai se il mio sguardo penetra questo fatal mister! *ecc.*	Woe if my gaze penetrates that fatal mystery! *etc.*
	RADAMES
Forse mi lesse nel pensier, *ecc.*	She has read my thoughts, *etc.*
	(seeing AIDA *enter)*
Dessa!	It is she!
	AMNERIS
Ei si turba . . . e quale sguardo rivolse a lei! Aida! A me rivale forse saria costei?	He is troubled . . . and how he looked at her! Aida! Could she be my rival?
	(to AIDA*)*
Vieni, o diletta, appressati; schiava non sei nè ancella qui dove in dolce fascino io ti chiamai sorella. Piangi? delle tue lacrime svela il segreto a me.	Come, my dearest, come hither; you are not slave nor handmaiden here where in sweet attraction I called you sister. You weep? Reveal the secret of your tears to me.
	AIDA
Ohimè! di guerra fremere l'atroce grido io sento. Per l'infelice patria, per me, per voi pavento.	Alas, I hear the terrible cry of war! For my unhappy country, for myself, for you I fear.

AMNERIS

Favelli il ver? nè s'agita più grave cura in te?	Do you tell the truth? No graver care disturbs you?

(to herself)

Trema, o rea schiava!	Tremble, O wicked slave!

RADAMES

(observing AMNERIS, *to himself)*

Nel volto a lei balena . . .	In her face flash . . .

AMNERIS

Ah, trema, rea schiava, trema . . .	Ah, tremble, wicked slave, tremble . . .

RADAMES

. . . lo sdegno ed il sospetto.	. . . anger and suspicion.

AMNERIS

. . . ch'io nel tuo cor discenda!	. . . lest I penetrate the secrets of your heart!

RADAMES

Guai se l'arcano affetto a noi leggesse in core!	Woe if she should read the secret love in our hearts!

AMNERIS

Trema che il ver m'apprenda quel pianto e quel rossor! Rea schiava, trema . . . ch'io nel tuo cor discenda . . . Ah, trema che il ver, *ecc.*	Tremble lest I learn the truth from that weeping and blushing! Wicked slave, tremble . . . lest into your heart I penetrate . . . Ah, tremble lest the truth, *etc.*

RADAMES

Guai se leggesse in cor, nel volto a lei balena lo sdegno ed il sospetto . . . Guai se l'arcano affetto, *ecc.*	Woe if she should read in our hearts, in her face flash anger and suspicion . . . Woe is our secret love, *etc.*

AIDA

Ah no! Sulla mia patria non geme il cor, il cor soltanto; quello ch'io verso è pianto di sventurato amor! Ah . . . è pianto, pianto di sventurato amor, *ecc.*	Ah no! Not alone for my country does my heart weep; the tears that I weep are tears of careless love! Ah . . . tears of careless love, *etc.*

(The* KING *enters, attended by* RAMFIS, *his Ministers, Priests and Captains.)

KING

Alta cagion v'aduna, of fidi egizii, al vostro re d'intorno. Dai confin d'Etiopia un messaggiero dianzi giungea. Gravi novelle ei reca . . . . Vi piaccia udirlo. Il messaggier s'avanzi!	A lofty cause brings you together, O loyal Egyptians, around your King. A messenger has just arrived from the Ethiopian borders. He brings serious news . . . . Be pleased to hear him. Let the messenger stand forth!

MESSENGER

Il sacro suolo dell'Egitto e invaso
dai barbari etiopi . . .
i nostri campi fùr devastati . . .
arse le messi . . .
e baldi della facil vittoria,
i predatori già
marciano su Tebe.

The sacred soil of Egypt is invaded
by Ethiopian barbarians . . .
our fields have been laid waste . . .
the crops burned . . .
and made bold by an easy victory,
the plunderers are already
marching on Thebes.

RADAMES, KING, RAMFIS, PRIESTS, MINISTERS, CAPTAINS

Ed osan tanto!

Do they dare so much!

MESSENGER

Un guerriero indomabile, feroce,
li conduce—Amonasro.

A warrior indomitable and fierce,
Amonasro, leads them.

RADAMES, KING, RAMFIS, PRIESTS, MINISTERS, CAPTAINS

Il re!

The King!

AIDA

(to herself)

Mio padre!

My father!

MESSENGER

Già Tebe è in armi
e dalle cento porte
sul barbaro invasore proromperà,
guerra recando e morte.

Thebes is already in arms,
and from its hundred gates will
rally forth to meet the barbarous
invader with war and death.

KING

Si: guerra e morte il nostro grido sia.

Ay! Let war and death be our cry!

RAMFIS, PRIESTS, MINISTERS, CAPTAINS

Guerra! . . . guerra! . . .
tremenda, inesorata.

War! . . . war! . . .
Terrible, unrelenting.

KING

Iside venerata
di nostre schiere invitte
già designava il condottier supremo:
Radamès!

Holy Isis has already named
the commander
of our invincible armies:
Radames!

AIDA, AMNERIS, MINISTERS, CAPTAINS

Radamès!

Radames!

RADAMES

Ah! sien grazie ai numi!
Son paghi i voti miei!

Ah, thanks be to the gods!
My prayers are answered!

AMNERIS

Ei duce! Ei duce!

He, the leader! He, the leader!

AIDA

Io tremo! Io tremo!

I tremble! I tremble!

MINISTERS *and* CAPTAINS

Radamès! Radamès!

Radames! Radames!

KING

Or, di Vulcano al tempio
muovi, o guerrier.
Le sacre armi ti cingi
alla vittoria vola.
Su! del Nilo al sacro lido
accorrete, egizii eroi,
da ogni cor prorompa il grido:
guerra e morte,
morte allo stranier!

Now go to Vulcan's temple,
O warrior.
Gird yourself with sacred arms
and speed to victory.
Arise! Hurry to the sacred banks
of the Nile, Egyptian heroes,
let the cry burst forth from every heart:
war and death,
death to the foreigner!

RAMFIS

Gloria ai numi!
Ognun rammenti
ch'essi reggono gli eventi,
che in poter de' numi solo
stan le sorti del guerrier.

Glory to the gods!
Let everyone remember
They decide the course of events;
The warrior's fortunes
rest solely in the hands of the gods.

MINISTERS *and* CAPTAINS

Su! del
Nilo al sacro lido
sien barriera i nostri petti;
non echeggi che un sol grido:
guerra, guerra e morte
allo stranier!

Arise!
To the sacred banks of the Nile
let our breasts form a barrier;
let there resound but a single cry:
war, war and death
to the foreigner!

RAMFIS

Ognun rammenti
che in poter dei numi solo
stan le sorti del guerra!

Let everyone remember
that the warrior's fortunes
rest solely in the hands of the gods!

KING

Su! su! del Nilo al sacro lido
accorrete, egizii eroi.
Da ogni cor prorompa un grido:
guerra e morte allo stranier!

Arise! Arise! Speed to the sacred
banks of the Nile, Egyptian heroes.
Let the cry resound from every heart:
war and death to the foreigner!

AIDA *(to herself)*

Per chi piango?
per chi piango?
per chi prego?
Qual poter m'avvince a lui!
Deggio amarlo ed e costui
un nemico, uno stranier!

For whom shall I weep?
For whom shall I weep?
For whom shall I pray?
What force binds me to him!
I must love him, and he is
and enemy, a foreigner!

RADAMES

Sacro fremito di gloria
tutta l'anima m'investe.
Su! corriamo alla vittoria!
Guerra, guerra e morte
allo stranier!

A sacred thrill of glory
fills my whole soul.
Arise! We will speed to victory!
War, war and death
to the foreigner!

AMNERIS

Di mia man ricevi, o duce
il vessillo glorioso;
ti sia guida, ti sia luce
della gloria sul sentier!

From my hand, O commander,
receive the glorious standard;
may it be your
guiding light on the road to glory!

KING, MINISTERS, CAPTAINS

Su! del Nilo al sacro lido, *ecc.*

Arise! To the sacred banks, *etc.*

RAMFIS *and* PRIESTS	
Gloria ai numi, *ecc.*	Glory to the gods, *etc.*
AMNERIS	
Ti sia guida, *ecc.*	May it be your guide, *etc.*
AIDA	
Per chi piango? *ecc.*	For whom shall I weep? *etc.*
RADAMES *and* MESSENGER	
Su! corriamo, *ecc.*	Arise! Let us speed, *etc.*
ALL	
Guerra! . . . Guerra! . . . Guerra!	War! . . . War! . . . War!
AIDA	
Deggio amarlo, e veggo in lui un nemico, uno stranier! Deggio amarlo, *ecc.*	I must love him, yet I see in him an enemy, a foreigner! I must love him, *etc.*
ALL THE OTHERS	
Guerra, guerra! sterminio! Sterminio all'invasor! Guerra, guerra, *ecc.*	War, war! Exterminate them! Exterminate them! War, war, *etc.*
AMNERIS *(turning to* RADAMES*)*	
Ritorna vincitor!	Return a conqueror!
ALL	
Ritorna vincitor!	Return a conqueror!
(All leave except AIDA*)*	
AIDA	
Ritorna vincitor! E dal mio labbro usci l'empia parola! Vincitor del padre mio . . . di lui che impugna l'armi per me . . . per ridonarmi una patria, una reggia e il nome illustre che qui celar m'è forza! Vincitor de' miei fratelli . . . ond'io lo vegga, tinto del sangue amato, trionfar nel plauso dell'egizie coorti! E dietro il carro, un re . . . mio padre . . . di catene avvinto! L'insana parola o numi, sperdete! Al seno d'un padre la figlia rendete; struggete, struggete, struggete le squadre dei nostri oppressor! Ah, sventurata! che dissi? e l'amor mio?	Return a conqueror! And from my lips came the unholy word! Conqueror of my father . . . of him who bears arms for me . . . to restore a country, a kingdom, and the illustrious name that I am forced to hide! Conqueror of my brothers . . . whence I might see him, stained with cherished blood, triumph in the boasting of the Egyptian cohorts! And behind his chariot, a king . . . my father . . . bound in chains! O gods, vanish the insane word! Restore a daughter to her father's breast; destroy, destroy, destroy the forces of our oppressor! Ah, wretched one! What did I say? And my love?

Dunque scordar poss'io questo fervido amore che, oppressa e schiava, come raggio di sol qui mi beava? Imprecherò la morte a Radamès . . . a lui ch'amo pur tanto! Ah! non fu in terra mai da più crudeli angoscie un core affranto! I sacri nomi di padre, d'amante ne proferir poss'io, ne ricordar. Per l'un, per l'altro, confusa, tremante, io piangere vorrei, vorrei pregar. Ma la mia prece in bestemmia si muta, delitto è il pianto a me, colpa il sospir. In notte cupa la mente è perduta, e nell'ansia crudel vorrei morir. Numi, pietà del mio soffrir! Speme non v'ha pel mio dolor. Amor fatal, tremendo amor spezzami il cor, fammi morir!	Can I then forget this fervent love which, like a shaft of sunlight, delighted me here although I am captive and a slave? Shall I call down death upon Radames . . . upon him whom I love so dearly! Ah! never on earth did anguish more cruel tear apart a heart! I cannot utter, nor yet recall The sacred names of father, of lover. For the one, for the other, confused, trembling, I would weep, I would pray. But my prayer turns to blasphemy; for me tears are a crime, sighs a fault. In darkest night my soul is lost, and in this cruel anguish I would die. O gods, have pity on my suffering! There is no hope for my sorrow. Fatal love, boundless love, break my heart, let me die!

Scene 2: Interior of the Temple of Vulcan at Memphis

(The High Priestess *and* Priestesses *are off-stage.)*

High Priestess

Possente, possente Fthà, del mondo spirito animator, ah! . . .	O mighty, mighty Ptah! spirit that animates the world, ah! . . .

High Priestess *and* Priestesses

. . . noi t'invochiamo!	. . . we invoke thee!

Ramfis *and* Priests

Tu che dal nulla hai tratto l'onde, la terra, il ciel, noi t'invochiamo!	Thou who from nothingness did create The earth, the sea and the sky, we invoke thee!

High Priestess

Immenso, immenso Fthà, del mondo spirito fecondator, ah! . . .	Phtha most high, universal creator of life, ah! . . .

High Priestess *and* Priestesses

. . . noi t'invochiamo!	. . . we invoke thee!

Ramfis *and* Priests

Nume che del tuo spirito sei figlio e genitor, noi t'invochiamo!	God, who of thy spirit art son and parent, we invoke thee!

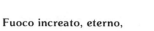

HIGH PRIESTESS

Fuoco increato, eterno, onde ebbe luce il sol, ah! . . .	Fire uncreated, eternal, whence the sun derived its light, ah! . . .

HIGH PRIESTESS *and* PRIESTESSES

. . . noi t'invochiamo!	. . . we call upon thee!

RAMFIS *and* PRIESTS

Vita dell'universo, mito d'eterno amor, noi t'invochiam!	Life of the universe, myth of eternal love, we call upon thee!

PRIESTESSES

Immenso Fthà!	Ptah most high!

PRIESTS

Noi t'invochiam!	We call upon thee!

Sacred Dance of the Priestesses

(RADAMES *enters and goes up to the altar.)*

PRIESTESSES

Immenso Fthà!	Ptah most high!

RAMFIS *and* PRIESTS

Noi t'invochiam!	We call upon thee!

RAMFIS
(to RADAMES*)*

Mortal, diletto ai numi, a te fidate son d'Egitto le sorti. Il sacro brando dal dio temprato, per tua man diventi ai nemici terror, folgore, morte.	Mortal, beloved of the gods, to you is entrusted the fate of Egypt. Let the sacred sword, tempered in heaven, bring terror, fire and death to our enemies.

PRIESTS

Il sacro brando, ecc.	Let the sacred sword, *etc.*

RAMFIS

Nume, custode e vindice di questa sacra terra, la mano tua distendi sovra l'egizio suol.	O god, guardian and avenger of this sacred land, extend thy hand over the land of Egypt.

RADAMES

Nume, che duce ed arbitro sei d'ogni umana guerra, proteggi tu, difendi d'Egitto il sacro suol.	O god, who dost rule and arbitrate in every human war, protect and defend the sacred land of Egypt.

RAMFIS

La mano tua, la mano tua distendi sovra l'egizio suol.	Thy hand, extend thy hand over the land of Egypt.

PRIESTS

Nume, custode e vindice di questa sacra terra . . .	O god, guardian and avenger of this sacred land . . .

RAMFIS *and* PRIESTS

Nume, custode ed arbitro di questa sacra terra, *ecc.*	O god, guardian and arbiter of this sacred land, *etc.*

RADAMES

Proteggi tu, *ecc.*	Do thou protect, *etc.*

PRIESTESSES

Possente, possente Ftha . . .	O mighty, mighty Ptah . . .

RADAMES, RAMFIS, PRIESTS

Possente Ftha . . .	O mighty Ptah . . .

PRIESTESSES

. . . del mondo creator . . .	. . . creator of the world . . .

RADAMES, RAMFIS, PRIESTS

. . . spirto fecondator . . .	. . . spirit of fertility . . .

RADAMES *and* RAMFIS

. . . tu che dal nulla hai tratto il mondo . . .	. . . thou who from nothing didst fashion the world . . .

PRIESTESSES

Ah! . . . Ah! . . .	Ah! . . . Ah! . . .

RAMFIS *and* PRIESTS

. . . tu che dal nulla hai tratto l'onde, la terra, il cielo . . .	. . . thou who from nothingness did create the earth, the sea and the sky . . .

RADAMES, RAMFIS, PRIESTS

. . . noi t'invochiamo!	. . . we call upon thee!

PRIESTESSES

Possente Fthà!	O mighty Ptah!

RADAMES, RAMFIS, PRIESTS

Tu che dal nulla hai tratto il mondo, noi t'invochiamo!	Thou who from nothingness did create the world, we call upon thee!

PRIESTESSES

Spirito animator . . .	Life-giving spirit . . .

RADAMES, RAMFIS, PRIESTS

. . . noi t'invochiam!	. . . we call upon thee!

PRIESTESSES

Spirto fecondator . . .	Spirit of fertility . . .

RADAMES, RAMFIS, PRIESTS

. . . noi t'invochiam!	. . . we invoke thee!

PRIESTESSES

Immenso Fthà! . . .	Ptah most high! . . . .

RADAMES, RAMFIS, PRIESTS

. . . noi t'invochiam!	. . . we invoke thee!

RADAMES *and* RAMFIS

Immenso Fthà! — Ptah most high!

RADAMES, RAMFIS, PRIESTESSES, PRIESTS

Immenso Fthà! — Ptah most high!

ACT II
Scene 1: In Amneris' apartments

Slaves are attiring AMNERIS ***for the triumphal feast.***

SLAVES

Chi mai, chi mai
fra gl'inni e i plausi,
erge alla gloria il vol,
al par d'un dio terribile,
fulgente al part del sol?
Vieni: sul crin ti piovano
contesti ai lauri i fior;
suonin di gloria i cantici
coi cantici d'amor.

Who is it,
that amidst hymns and praises,
soars to glory
like a mighty god,
shining like the sun?
Come: let flowers laced with
laurel shower upon your hair;
let hymns of glory sound
with songs of love.

AMNERIS

Ah! vieni, vieni, amor mio,
m'inebbria,
fammi beato il cor!

Ah, come, my love,
enrapture me,
fill my heart with happiness!

SLAVES

Or dove son le barbare
orde dello stranier?
Siccome nebbia sparvero
al soffio del guerrier.
Vieni: di gloria il premio
raccogli, o vincitor;
t'arrise la vittoria,
t'arriderà l'amor.

Where now are the barbarous hordes
of the invader?
Like a mist they scattered
at the warrior's breath.
Come, O conqueror,
collect the reward for glory;
victory has already smiled on you,
love will smile upon you now.

AMNERIS

Ah! vieni, vieni, amor mio, ravvivami
d'un caro accento ancor!

Ah, come, my love, restore me to life
with one tender word!

Dance of the Moorish Slaves

SLAVES

Vieni: sul crin ti piovano
contesti ai lauri i fior, *ecc* . . .
. . . coi cantici d'amor!

Come: let flowers laced with
laurel shower upon your hair, *etc* . . .
. . . with songs of love!

AMNERIS

Ah! vieni, vieni, amor mio,
m'inebbria, *ecc.*
Silenzio! Aida verso noi s'avanza.
Figlia de' vinti
il suo dolor m'è sacro.

Ah, come my love,
enrapture me, *etc.*
Silence! Aida approaches us.
She is the daughter of the vanquished
and I respect her sorrow.

(The slaves go out. AIDA *enters.)*

Nel rivederla, il dubbio
atroce in me si desta.
Il mistero fatal si squarci alfine!

Seeing her gain,
arouses doubt in me.
Let the fatal secret be revealed at last.

(to AIDA*)*

Fu la sorte dell'armi
a' tuoi funesta, povera Aida!
Il lutto che ti pesa
sul cor teco divido.
Io son l'amica tua . . .
tutto da me tu avrai . . .
vivrai felice!

Fate was cruel
to your people, poor Aida!
I share with you
the grief that burdens your heart.
I am your friend . . .
you shall have everything of me . . .
you shall live happily!

AIDA

Felice esser poss'io
lungi dal suol natio . . .
qui dove ignota m'è la sorte
del padre e dei fratelli?

How can I be happy
far from my homeland . . .
here where I do not know
the fate of father and brothers?

AMNERIS

Ben ti compiango!
Pure hanno un confine
i mali di quaggiù . . . .
Sanerà il tempo
le angoscie del tuo core,
e più che il tempo,
un dio possente . . . amore.

How I pity you!
Yet earthly sorrows
have a limit . . . .
Time will heal
your heart's grief
and, more than time,
a mighty god . . . love.

AIDA

Amore, amore! gaudio, tormento,
soave ebbrezza, ansia crudel.
Ne' tuoi dolori
la vita io sento;
un tuo sorriso
mi schiude il ciel!
Ne' tuoi dolori, *ecc.*

Love, love! joy, torment,
sweet rapture, cruel anguish.
In thy pangs
I feel life;
a smile from thee
unlocks heaven to me!
In thy pangs, *etc.*

AMNERIS

Ah! quel pallore, quel turbamento
svelan l'arcana febbre d'amor.
D'interrogarla quasi ho sgomento.
Divido l'ansie del suo terror!

Ah, that pallor, that agitation
reveal the hidden fever of love.
I am almost afraid to question her.
I share her pangs of terror!

(to AIDA*)*

Ebben: qual nuovo fremito
t'assal, gentil Aida?
I tuoi segreti svelami,
all'amor mio t'affida.
Tra i forti che pugnarono
della tua patria a danno,
qualcuno, un dolce affano,
forse a te in cor destò?

Well, what new fears
assail you now, gentle Aida?
Reveal your secrets to me,
trust in my affection.
Among the warriors who fought
against your country,
someone, perhaps, has aroused
sweet concern in your heart?

AIDA

Che parli?

What are you saying?

AMNERIS

A tutti barbara
non si mostrò la sorte,
se in campo il duce impavido
cadde trafitto a morte.

Fate has not been
unkind to all,
although on the field of battle
the fearless leader fell mortally wounded.

Aida

Che mai dicesti! misera!	Oh, what have you said! Alas!

Amneris

Che mai dicesti! misera!	Oh, what have you said! Alas!

Amneris

Si, Radamès da, tuoi fu spento . . .	Yes, Radames has been slain by your people

Aida

Misera!	Woe!

Amneris

E pianger puoi?	And you can weep?

Aida

Per sempre io piangerò!	I shall weep forever!

Amneris

Gli dei t'han vendicata.	The gods have avenged you.

Aida

Avversi sempre a me furo i numi.	The gods were always against me.

Amneris

Trema! in cor ti lessi . . . tu l'ami.	Tremble! I have read it in your heart . . . you love him.

Aida

Io!	I!

Amneris

Non mentire! Un detto ancora e il vero saprò. Fissami in volto . . . io t'ingannava . . . Radamès vive.	Do not lie! One more word and I shall know the truth. Look me straight in the face. I deceived you . . . Radames lives.

Aida

Vive! Ah, grazie, o numi!	Lives! Ah, thank you, gods!

Amneris

E ancor mentir tu speri? Si, tu l'ami. Ma l'amo anch'io, intendi tu? Son tua rivale, figlia de' Faraoni.	And you still hope to lie? Yes, you love him. But I also love him, do you understand? I, daughter of the Pharaohs, am your rival.

Aida

Mia rivale! ebben sia pure . . . Anch'io son tal . . .	My rival! Well, even so . . . I, also, am . . .

***(checking herself and falling at the feet of* Amneris)**

Ah! che dissi mai? Pietà! Perdono! Ah! pietà ti prenda del mio dolor. È vero, io l'amo d'immenso amor. Tu sei felice, tu sei possente, io vivo solo per questo amor!	Ah, whatever have I said? Mercy! Pardon! Ah! Have pity on my sorrow! It is true, I love him passionately. You are happy, you are powerful, I live only for this love!

AMNERIS

Trema, vil schiava! Spezza il tuo core . . . segnar tua morte può quest'amore. Del tuo destino arbitra sono, d'odio e vendetta le furie ho in cor.	Tremble, wicked slave! Your heart is breaking . . . this love can mean your death. I am judge of your fate, a fury of hate and vengeance is in my heart.

AIDA

Tu sei felice, tu sei possente, *ecc.*	You are happy, you are powerful, *etc.*

AMNERIS

Trema, vil schiava! *ecc.*	Tremble, wicked slave! *etc.*

SOLDIERS *and* PEOPLE
(heard in the distance)

Su! del Nilo al sacro lido sien barriera i nostri petti; non echeggi che un sol grido: guerra, guerra e morte allo stranier!	Arise! To the sacred banks of the Nile let a barrier be formed by our breasts; let a single cry resound: war, war and death to the invader!

AMNERIS

Alla prompa che s'appresta, meco, o schiava, assiterai; tu prostrata nella polvere, io sul trono accanto al re.	O slave, you will be present at the parade which is being prepared; you prostrate in the dust, I on the throne beside the King.

AIDA

Ah! pietà! Che più mi resta? Un deserto è la mia vita, vivi e regna, il tuo furore io tra breve placherò. Quest'amore che t'irrita nella tomba spegnerò.	Ah, mercy! What more is left to me? My life is a desert; live and reign, I shall soon placate your rage. I will extinguish this love that angers you in the tomb.

AMNERIS

Vien, mi segui, apprenderai se lottar tu puoi con me! Apprenderai, *ecc.*	Come, follow me; you will learn if you can fight against me! You will learn, *etc.*

AIDA

Ah! pietà! Quest'amor nella tomba io spegnerò!	Ah! mercy! I will extinguish this love in the tomb!

SOLDIERS *and* PEOPLE

Guerra e morte! Guerra e morte allo stranier!	War and death! War and death to the invader!

AIDA

Pietà! . . . Pietà!	Mercy! . . . Mercy!

AMNERIS

Vieni, mi segui e apprenderai se lottar tu puoi con me.	Come, follow me, and you will learn if you can fight against me.

SOLDIERS *and* PEOPLE

Guerra e morte allo stranier!	War and death to the invader!

AIDA

Numi, pietà del mio martir,	Gods, have pity on my agony;
speme non v'ha pel mio dolor.	I have no hope in my distress.
Numi, pietà del mio soffrir.	Gods, have pity on my suffering.
Numi, pietà, pietà, pietà.	Gods, have pity.

Scene 2: An Avenue at the Gates of Thebes

A tall obelisk with a throne at its base. The* KING, *followed by the entire court, enters and takes his place upon the throne.

PEOPLE

Gloria all'Egitto, ad Iside	Glory to Egypt, and to Isis
che il sacro suol protegge!	who protects its sacred soil!
Al re che il Delta regge	Let us raise festive hymns
inni festosi alziam!	to the king who rules the Delta!
Gloria! Gloria! Gloria al re! Gloria!	Glory! Glory! Glory to the King! Glory!
Inni alziam, *ecc.*	Let us raise hymns, *etc.*

WOMEN

S'intrecci il loto al lauro	Let lotus be laced with laurel
sul crin dei vincitori!	upon the heads of the conquerors!
Nembo gentil di fiori	Let a sweet shower of flowers
stenda sull'armi un vel.	veil the arms of war.
Danziam, fanciulle egizie,	Let us dance, Egyptian maidens,
le mistiche carole,	the mystic dances,
come d'intorno al sole	as the stars dance eternally
danzano gli astri in ciel . . .	around the sun in the sky . . .

PRIESTS

Della vittoria agl'arbitri	Raise your eyes
supremi il guardo ergete;	to the supreme arbiters of victory;
grazie agli dei rendete	give thanks to the gods
nel fortunato di.	on this happy day.

WOMEN

Come d'intorno al sole	As, the stars dance
danzano gli astri in ciel.	around the sun in the sky.

MEN

Inni festosi alziam al re.	Let us raise festive hymns to the King.

PRIESTS

Grazie agli dei rendete	Give thanks to the gods
nel fortunato di.	this happy day.

(The troops march past the* KING. *Dancing girls appear, carrying the spoils of victory. Other troops enter, behind war chariots, banners, sacred vessels and images of the gods.)

PEOPLE

Vieni, o guerriero vindice . . .	Come, victorious warrior . . .

PRIESTS

Agli arbitri supremi . . .	To the supreme arbiters . . .

PEOPLE

. . . vieni a gioir con noi . . .	. . . come and rejoice with us . . .

PRIESTS

. . . il guardo ergete,
il guardo ergete.

. . . raise your eyes,
raise your eyes.

PEOPLE

. . . sul passo degli eroi
i lauri, i fior versiam!

. . . in the heroes' path
laurels and flowers let us cast!

PRIESTS

Grazie agli dei rendete
nel fortunato di.

Give thanks to the gods
this happy day.

PEOPLE

Vieni, o guerrier,
vieni a gioir con noi, *ecc.*
Gloria, gloria, gloria al guerrier, *ecc.*

Come, O warrior,
come and rejoice with us, *etc.*
Glory, glory, glory to the warrior, *etc.*

PRIESTS

Grazie, grazie, grazie agli dei, *ecc.*

Thanks, thanks to the gods, *etc.*

*(*RADAMES *enters under a canopy carried by twelve officers.)*

PEOPLE

Gloria, gloria all'Egitto, *ecc.*

Glory, glory to Egypt, *etc.*

PRIESTS

Grazie agli dei rendete, *ecc.*

Give thanks unto the gods, *etc.*

(The KING *descends from the throne to enbrace* RADAMES*)*

KING

Salvator della patria, io ti saluto.
Vieni, e mia figlia
di sua man ti porga
il serto trionfale.

Savior of our country, I salute you.
Come, that my daughter
may with her own hand
present the triumphal laurel.

*(*RADAMES *bows before* AMNERIS*, who hands him the laurel crown.)*

Ora a me chiedi
quanto piu brami.
Nulla a te negato
sarà in tal di: lo giuro
per la corona mia, pei sacri numi.

Now you ask of me
whatever you most desire.
Nothing shall be denied you
on such a day; I swear it
by my crown and by the sacred gods.

RADAMES

Concedi in pria
che innanzi a te sien tratti
i prigionier.

First permit
the prisoners to be
brought before you.

(Ethiopian prisoners are brought in, AMONASRO *last.)*

RAMFIS *and* PRIESTS

Grazie agli dei,
grazie rendete nel fortunato di.
Grazie, grazie agli dei!

Thanks be to the gods,
give thanks upon this happy day.
Give thanks to the gods!

AIDA

Che veggo! Egli? Mio padre!

What do I see? Is it he? My father!

AMNERIS, RADAMES, RAMFIS, KING, PRIESTS, PEOPLE

Suo padre!

Her father!

AMNERIS

In poter nostro!	In our power!

AIDA
(embracing her father)

Tu! Prigionier!	You! A prisoner!

AMONASRO
(softly to AIDA*)*

Non mi tradir!	Do not betray me!

KING
(to AMONASRO*)*

T'appressa. Dunque tu sei . . . ?	Come forward. So you are . . .?

AMONASRO

Suo padre. Anch'io pugnai . . . vinti noi fummo . . . morte invan cercai. Quest'assisa ch'io vesto vi dica che il mio re, la mia patria ho difeso; fu la sorte a nostr'armi nemica, tornò vano de' forti l'ardir. Al mio piè nella polve disteso giacque il re da più colpi trafitto; se l'amor della patria è delitto siam rei tutti, siam pronti a morir! Ma tu, re, tu signore possente, a costoro ti volgi clemente. Oggi noi siam percossi dal fato, ah! doman voi potria il fato colpir.	Her father. I too have fought . . . we were conquered . . . I sought death in vain. This uniform I wear may tell you I fought for my country and my King; fate was hostile to our arms, the courage of the valiant was in vain. At my feet, stretched in the dust, lay the King, wounded by many blows; if love of country be a crime all of us are guilty, we are ready to die! But you, O King, you, O mighty lord, have mercy on these men. Today we are struck down by fate, but tomorrow fate may strike at you.

AIDA

Ma tu, re, tu signore possente, a costoro ti volgi clemente. Oggi noi siam percossi dal fato.	But you, O King, you, O mighty lord, have mercy on these men. Today we are struck down by fate.

SLAVES *and* PRISONERS

Si, dai numi percossi noi siamo; tua pieta, tua clemenza imploriamo. Ah! giammai di soffrir vi sia dato cio . . .	Yes, by the gods we are struck down; we ask for your mercy. Ah, may you never have to suffer . . .

AIDA *and* AMONASRO

Ah! doman voi potria il fato colpir.	Ah! tomorrow fate may strike you.

SLAVES *and* PRISONERS

. . . che in oggi n'è dato soffrir!	. . . what we must suffer today!

RAMFIS *and* PRIESTS

Struggi, o re, queste ciurme feroci, chiudi il cor allae perfide voci; fur dai numi votati all morte, or de' numi si compia il voler!	Crush, O King, this savage rabble, close your heart to their perfidious voices; They were condemned to death by the gods, now let the will of the gods be done!

AIDA, SLAVES, PRISONERS

Pietà! . . . Pietà! . . . Pietà!	Mercy! . . . Mercy! . . . Mercy!

AIDA

Ma tu, o re, signor possente,
a costoro ti mostra clemente.

But you, O King, O powerful lord,
your mercy to these men.

AMNERIS

Quali sguardi sovr'essa ha rivolti!
Di qual fiamma balenano i volti!

What glances he now casts upon her!
What a flame burns in their eyes!

AMONASRO

Oggi noi siam percossi dal fato,
voi doman potria il fato colpir.

Today we are struck down by fate,
but tomorrow fate may strike at you.

RAMFIS *and* PRIESTS

A morte! A morte! A morte!
O re, struggi queste ciurme.

To death! To death! To death!
O king, crush this rabble.

KING

Or che fausti ne arridon gli eventi
a costoro mostriamci clementi.

Since fate smiles happily upon us,
show mercy to these men.

SLAVES *and* PRISONERS

Tua pietade, tua clemenza imploriamo.
Ah! pietà . . . tua clemenza imploriamo.

We ask for your mercy.
Ah! mercy . . . we ask for your mercy.

PEOPLE

Sacerdoti, gli sdegni placate;
l'umil prece ascolate.

Oh, you priests, now calm your anger;
listen to their humble prayer.

RADAMES
(watching AIDA)

Il dolor che in quel volto favella
al mio sguardo la rende più bella;
ogni stilla del pianto adorato
nel mio petto ravviva l'amore, *ecc.*

The sorrow which speaks in that face
makes her more lovely in my sight;
every tear she sheds
reawakens love in my breast, *etc.*

AMNERIS

Quali sguardi sovr'essa ha rivolti!
Di qual fiamma balenano i volti!
Ed io sola, avvilita, reietta?
La vendetta mi rugge nel cor, *ecc.*

What glances he now casts upon her!
What a flame burns in their eyes!
And I alone, reviled, rejected?
Vengeance cries out within my hear, *etc.*

AMONASRO

Tua pieta, tua clemenza imploriamo, *ecc.*

We ask for your mercy, *etc.*

KING

Or che fausti ne arridon, *ecc.*

Since fate smiles propitiously, *etc.*

AIDA

Tua pietà imploro.
Oggi noi siam percossi, *ecc.*

I ask for your mercy.
Today we are struck down, *etc.*

RAMFIS *and* PRIESTS

Si compisca de' numi il voler!
Struggi, o re, queste cirume, *ecc.*

Let the will of the gods be accomplished!
Crush, O King, this rabble, *etc.*

SLAVES *and* PRISONERS

Pietà . . . ah! pietà, *ecc.*

Mercy . . . ah! pity, *etc.*

PEOPLE

Sacerdoti, gli sdegni placate!
L'umil prece de' vinti
ascoltate, *ecc.*

O priests, calm your anger!
Listen to the humble prayers
of the vanquished, *etc.*

AIDA *and* AMONASRO

Ma tu, o re, tu signore possente, *ecc.*	But you, O King, O mighty lord, *etc.*

RADAMES

Il dolor, *ecc.*	The sorrow, *etc.*

KING

La pietà, *ecc.*	Mercy, *etc.*

SLAVES *and* PRISONERS

Si, dai numi percossi noi siamo, *ecc.*	Yes, by the gods we are struck down, *etc.*

PEOPLE

Re possente, re possente!	O mighty King!

RAMFIS *and* PRIESTS

Struggi, o re, queste ciurme, *ecc.*	Crush, O King, this savage rabble, *etc.*

AMNERIS

Ed io sola avvilita, *ecc.*	And I alone, reviled, *etc.*

RAMFIS *and* PRIESTS

Struggi, o re . . .	O King, crush . . .

AIDA

Doman voi il fato, *ecc.*	Tomorrow fate, *etc.*

RADAMES

Ogni stilla, *ecc.*	Every tear, *etc.*

AMNERIS

Ed io solla, *ecc.*	And I alone, *etc.*

AMONASRO

Oggi noi, *ecc.*	Today we, *etc.*

KING

La pietà, *ecc.*	Mercy, *etc.*

SLAVES *and* PRISONERS

Ah, giammai, *ecc.*	Ah, never, *etc.*

PEOPLE

E tu, o re, *ecc.*	And you, O King, *etc.*

RAMFIS *and* PRIESTS

Struggi, o re, *ecc.*	O King, crush, *etc.*

RADAMES

O re, pei sacri numi, per lo splendor della tua corona, compier giurasti il voto mio . . .	O King, by the sacred gods, by the splendor of your crown, you swore to grant my wish . . .

KING

Giurai.	I swore.

RADAMES

Ebbene: a te pei prigionieri etiopi vita domando e liberta.	Well then: I ask of you life and freedom for the Ethiopian prisoners.

AMNERIS
(to herself)

Per tutti!	For all of them!

PRIESTS

Morte ai nemici della patria!	Death to our country's enemies!

PEOPLE

Grazia per gl'infelici!	Mercy for these wretched ones!

RAMFIS

Ascolta, o re. Tu pure, giovine eroe, saggio consiglio ascolta: Son nemici e prodi sono; la vendetta hanno nel cor, fatti audaci dal perdono correranno all'armi ancor!	Hear me, O King. You too, young hero, hear wise advice: They are enemies, and they are valiant; they harbor vengeance in their hearts; emboldened by pardon they will hasten to take up arms once again!

RADAMES

Spento Amonasro il re guerrier, non resta speranza ai vinti	With Amonasro, their warrior king dead, no hope is left to the conquered.

RAMFIS

Almeno, arra di pace e securta, fra noi resti col padre Aida.	At least, as pledge of peace and security, let Aida and her father remain among us.

KING

Al tuo consiglio io cedo. Di securtà, di pace un miglior pegno or io vo' darvi. Radames, la patria tutto a te deve. D'Amneris la mano premio ti sia. Sovra l'Egitto un giorno con essa regnerai.	I yield to your counsel. Now I will give you a better promise of peace and security. Radames, our country owes everything to you. May the hand of Amneris be your reward. One day you will reign with her over Egypt.

AMNERIS
(to herself)

Venga la schiava, venga a rapirmi l'amor mio . . . se l'osa!	Now, let the slave come, let her come and take my love from me . . . if she dare!

KING *and* PEOPLE

Gloria all'Egitto, ad Iside che il sacro suol difende, s'intrecci il loto al lauro sul crin del vincitor.	Glory to Egypt, and to Isis who defends that sacred land, let lotus be laced with laurel upon the heads of the conquerors.

SLAVES *and* PRISONERS

Gloria al clemente egizio che i nostri ceppi ha sciolto, che ci ridona ai liberi solchi del patrio suol.	Glory to the merciful Egyptian who has loosed our chains, who returns us to our free, native fields.

RAMFIS *and* PRIESTS

Inni leviamo ad Iside che il sacro suol difende! Preghiam che i fati arridano fausti alla patria ognor.	Let us raise hymns to Isis, who defends our sacred land! Let us pray that the fates may ever smile happily on our country.

AIDA
(to herself)

Qual speme omai più restami?
A lui la gloria, il trono . . .
a me l'oblio,
le lacrime d'un disperato amor.

What hope now is left to me?
For him, glory, the throne . . .
for me, oblivion,
the tears of a hopeless love.

RADAMES
(to himself)

D'avverso nume il folgore
sul capo mio discende.
Ah no! d'Egitto il soglio
non val d'Aida il cor.

The wrath of a hostile god
descends upon my head.
Ah no! The throne of Egypt
is not worth the heart of Aida.

AMNERIS
(to herself)

Dall'inatteso giubilo
inebbriata io sono;
tutti in un dì
si compiono i sogni del mio cor.

I am intoxicated,
with this unexpected joy;
all my heart's dreams are fulfilled
in one day.

KING *and* PEOPLE

Gloria . . . ad Iside!

Glory . . . to Isis!

RAMFIS

Preghiam che i fati . . .
preghiam che i fati arridano
fausti alla patria ognor,

Let us pray that the fates . . .
let us pray that the fates may always
smile happily on our land.

AMONASRO
(to AIDA*)*

Fa cor: della tua patria
i lieti eventi aspetta;
per noi della vendetta
già prossimo è l'albor.

Take heart: await happier events
for your country;
the dawn of vengeance
is already near.

RADAMES

Qual inatteso folgore
sul capo mio discende!

What an unexpected blow
descends upon my head!

AMNERIS

Tutti in un dì si compiono le gioie
del mio cor.

All my heart's joy
is fulfilled in one day.

KING

Gloria all'Egitto!

Glory to Egypt!

AMONASRO

Fa cor, fa cor!

Take heart, take heart!

RAMFIS *and* PRIESTS

Inni leviam ad Iside.

Let us raise hymns to Isis.

AIDA

A me l'oblio, le lacrime.

For me, oblivion, tears.

PEOPLE

Gloria all'Egitto!

Glory to Egypt!

AIDA

Ah! qual speme omai più restami? *ecc.*

Ah! what hope now is left to me? *etc.*

AMNERIS

Ah! dall'inatteso gaudio, *ecc.*	Ah! with this unexpected joy, *etc.*

RADAMES

Ah! qual inatteso folgore, *ecc.*	Ah! what an unexpected blow, *etc.*

AMONASRO

Ah! fa cor, *ecc.*	Ah! take heart, *etc.*

KING *and* PEOPLE

Gloria all'Egitto, ad Iside, *ecc.*	Glory to Egypt, and to Isis, *etc.*

RAMFIS *and* PRIESTS

Inni leviamo ad Iside, *ecc.*	Let us raise hymns to Isis, *etc.*

SLAVES *and* PRISONERS

Gloria al clemente egizio, *ecc.*	Glory to the merciful Egyptian, *etc.*

ACT III
On the Banks of the Nile

A moonlit night outside the temple of Isis.

PRIESTS
(from within the temple)

O tu che sei d'Osiride madre immortale e sposa, diva che i casti palpiti desti agli umani in cor . . .	O thou who art of Osiris both mother and immortal bride, goddess who awakest pure emotions in the human heart . . .

HIGH PRIESTESS

. . . soccorri, soccorri a noi . . .	. . . grant us help . . .

PRIESTS

. . . soccorri a noi pietosa, madre d'immenso amor . . .	. . . grant us merciful help, O mother of great love . . .

PRIESTS *and* PRIESTESSES

. . . soccori a noi.	. . . grant us help.

(AMNERIS *arrives by boat accompanied by her suite and* RAMFIS.)

RAMFIS
(to AMNERIS*)*

Vieni d'Iside al tempio; alla vigilia delle tue nozze invoca della diva il favore. Iside legge de' mortali nel core; ogni mistero degli umani a lei noto.	Come to the temple of Isis; on the eve of your wedding call on the favor of the goddess. Isis knows the hearts of mortals; every human secret is known to her.

AMNERIS

Si; io pregherò che Radamès mi doni tutto il suo cor, come il mio cor a lui sacro è per sempre.	Yes; I will pray that Radames may give me his whole heart, as mine is dedicated to him alone forever.

RAMFIS

Andiamo.
Pregherai fino all'alba;
io sarò teco.

Let us go.
You will pray till break of day;
I will be with you.

PRIESTESSES

Soccorri, soccorri a noi . . .

Grant us, grant us help . . .

PRIESTS

Soccorri a noi pietosa,
madre d'immenso amor . . .

Grant us merciful help,
O mother of great love . . .

PRIESTS *and* PRIESTESSES

. . . soccorri a noi.

. . . grant us help.

(AMNERIS *and* RAMFIS *go into the temple.)*

AIDA
(approaching cautiously)

Qui Radamès verrà!
Che vorrà dirmi?
Io tremo!
Ah! se tu vieni a recarmi,
o crudel, l'ultimo addio,
del Nilo i cupi vortici
mi daran tomba,
e pace forse
e oblio.

Radames is coming here!
What can he want to say to me?
I tremble!
Ah! If you should come,
O cruel one, to bid me a last farewell,
the dark swirling waters of the Nile
will be my grave,
and bring me peace, perhaps,
and oblivion.

O patria mia,
mai più ti rivedrò! . . .
O cieli azzurri, o dolci aure native,
dove sereno
il mio mattin brillò;
o verdi colli, o profumate rive,
o patria mia,
mai piu ti rivedrò!
O patria mia, mai più,
ah! mai più ti rivedrò! *ecc.*
mai più, no, no, mai più!
O fresche valli,
o queto asil beato
che un di promesso dall'amor mi fu!
Or che d'amore il sogno è dileguato,
o patria mia,
non ti vedrò mai più! *ecc.*
O patria mia,
mai più ti rivedrò!

O, my homeland,
I will never see you again! . . .
O blue skies, O soft native breezes,
where the light of my youth
quietly sparkled;
O, green hills, perfumed shores,
O, my homeland,
I will never see you again!
O my homeland, never again,
ah! I will never see you . . . *etc.*
never again, never again!
O, cool valleys,
O, blessed, tranquil refuge
which once was promised me by love!
Now that the dream of love has faded,
O, my homeland,
I will never see you again! *etc.*
O, my homeland,
I will never see you again!

(AMONASRO *enters.)*

Ciel! mio padre!

Heavens! My father!

AMONASRO

A te grave cagion m'adduce, Aida.
Nulla sfugge al mio sguardo.
D'amor ti struggi per Radamès,
ei t'ama,
qui lo attendi.
Dei Faraon la figlia
è tua rivale . . .
razza infame, aborrita e a noi fatale!

A serious cause brings me to you, Aida.
Nothing escapes my notice.
You are consumed with love for Radames,
he loves you,
you are waiting for him here.
The daughter of the Pharaohs
is your rival . . .
an accursed race, abhorred, fatal to us!

AIDA

E in suo potere io sto!
Io d'Amonasro figlia!

And I am in her power!
I, Amonasro's daughter!

AMONASRO

In poter di lei! No! se lo brami
la possente rival tu vincerai,
e patria, e trono, e amor,
tutto tu avrai.
Rivedrai
le foreste imbalsamate,
le fresche valli, i nostri templi d'ôr!

In her power! No! If you wish it,
you shall conquer your powerful rival,
and country, throne and love,
you shall have them all.
You shall see once more
the perfumed forests,
the cool valleys and our golden temples!

AIDA

Rivedrò le foreste imbalsamate,
le nostri valli, i nostri tempii d'ôr.

I shall see once more
the perfumed forests . . .

AMONASRO

Sposa felice a lui che amasti tanto,
tripudii immensi ivi potrai gioir.

Happy wife to him you love so much,
there you will be able to enjoy untold happiness . . .

AIDA

Un giorno solo
di si dolce incanto,
un'ora, un'ora di tal gioia,
e poi morir!

One single day
of such sweet enchantment,
one hour, one hour of such a joy,
and then to die!

AMONASRO

Pur rammenti
che a noi l'egizio immite,
le case, i tempii e l'are profanò;
trasse in ceppi le vergini rapite;
madri, vecchi, fanciulli ei trucidò.

But remember
the Egyptian has desecrated
our homes, our temples and our altars;
carried our virgins off in chains;
murdered mothers, old men, children.

AIDA

Ah! ben rammento
quegl'infausti giorni!
Rammento i lutti
che il mio cor soffri!
Deh! fate, o numi, che per noi ritorni . . .

Ah! I remember well
those unhappy days!
I remember the grief
in my heart!
O gods, let the . . .

AMONASRO

Rammenta.

Remember.

AIDA

. . . che per noi ritorni l'alba
invocata de' sereni dì.

. . . dawn of happy days
return for us.

AMONASRO

Non fia che tardi.
In armi ora si desta
il popol nostro; tutto è pronto già.
Vittoria avrem. Solo a saper mi resta
qual sentier il nemico seguirà.

Let it not be delayed.
Our people are ready to rise
in arms; all is ready.
Victory will be ours. The only thing left
for me to know is what route the enemy will follow.

AIDA

Chi scoprirlo potria? Chi mai?

Who could ever discover it? Who?

AMONASRO

Tu stessa!

You yourself!

AIDA

Io?

I?

AMONASRO

Radamès so che
qui attendi.
Ei t'ama,
ei conduce gli egizii . . . .
Intendi?

I know you are waiting
for Radames here.
He loves you,
and he commands the Egyptians . . . .
You understand?

AIDA

Orrore! Che mi consigli tu?
No! No! giammai!

Horror! What are you asking?
No! No! Never!

AMONASRO

Su, dunque! sorgete,
egizie coorti!
col fuoco struggete
le nostre città!
Spargete il terrore,
le stragi, le morti,
al vostro furore
più freno non v'ha.

Then come, arise,
Egyptian cohorts;
destroy our cities
with fire!
Spread terror,
carnage and death.
There is no obstacle
now to your fury.

AIDA

Ah! padre! padre!

Ah! Father! Father!

AMONASRO

Mia figlia ti chiami!

You call yourself my daughter!

AIDA

Pietà! pietà! pietà!

Mercy! Mercy!

AMONASRO

Flutti di sangue scorrono
sulle citta dei vinti.
Vedi? Dai negri vortici
si levano gli estinti,
ti additan essi e gridano:
"Per te la patria muor!"

Rivers of blood engulf
the cities of the conquered.
Do you see? From the black whirlpools
the dead arise
and point at you, crying:
"Because of you your homeland perishes!"

AIDA

Pietà! pietà! padre, pietà!

Mercy! Mercy! Father, have mercy!

AMONASRO

Una larva orribile
fra l'ombre a noi s'affaccia.
Trema! Le scarne braccia . . .

A dreadful phantom from among
the shadows appears before us.
Tremble! Its fleshless arms . . .

AIDA

Ah!

Ah!

AMONASRO

. . . sul capo tuo levò . . .

. . . it has raised above your head . . .

AIDA

Padre!

Father!

AMONASRO

Tua madre ell'è . . .

It is your mother . . .

AIDA

No!

No!

AMONASRO

. . . ravvisala . . .

. . . see her . . .

AIDA

Ah!

Ah!

AMONASRO

. . . ti maledice.

. . . she is cursing you.

AIDA

Ah! no! Ah! no! Padre, pietà! pietà!

Ah no! Father, have mercy! Mercy!

AMONASRO

Non sei mia figlia.
Dei Faraoni tu sei la schiava!

You are not my daughter.
You are a slave of the Pharoahs!

AIDA

Ah!
Pietà! . . . pietà! pietà!
Padre! a costoro schiava non sono.
Non maledirmi,
non imprecarmi . . .
Ancor tua figlia
potrai chiamarmi . . .
della mia patria degna sarò.

Ah!
Have mercy . . . have mercy!
Father, I am not their slave.
Do not curse me,
do not reject me . . .
You will still be able
to call me daughter . . .
I will be worthy of my native land.

AMONASRO

Pensa che un popolo,
vinto, straziato,
per te soltanto risorger può.

Remember that a people,
conquered and tormented,
can rise again because of you.

AIDA

O patria! O patria, quanto mi costi!

O my country, what you have cost me!

AMONASRO

Coraggio! Ei giunge.
Là tutto udrò.

Courage! He is coming.
From there I shall hear everything.

(He conceals himself among the palm trees. RADAMES *enters.)*

RADAMES

Pur ti riveggo, mia dolce Aida.

Once more I see you, my sweet Aida.

AIDA

T'arresta. Vanne.
Che speri ancor?

Stop. Go away.
What can you yet hope for?

RADAMES

A te dappresso l'amore mi guida.

Love leads me to you.

AIDA

Te i riti attendono d'un altro amor.
D'Amneris sposo . . .

The rites of another love await you.
Husband of Amneris . . .

RADAMES

Che parli mai?
Te sola, Aida, te deggio amar.
Gli dei m'ascoltano, tu mia sarai.

What are you saying?
I must love only you, Aida.
The gods hear me; you shall be mine.

AIDA

D'uno spergiuro non ti macchiar!
Prode t'amai, no t'amerei spergiuro.

Do not stain yourself with a lie!
I loved you, I would not love you a liar.

RADAMES

Dell'amor mio dubiti, Aida?

Do you question my love, Aida?

AIDA

E come speri sottrarti
d'Amneris ai vezzi,
del re al voler,
del tuo popolo ai voti,
dei sacerdoti all'ira?

And how do you hope to escape
the charms of Amneris,
the will of the King,
the wishes of your people,
and the wrath of the priests?

RADAMES

Odimi, Aida.
Nel fiero anelito di nuova guerra
il suol Etiope
si ridestò.
I tuoi gia invadono la nostra terra,
io degli egizii duce saro.
Fra il suon,
fra i plausi della vittoria,
al re mi prostro,
gli svelo il cor.
Sarai tu il serto della mia gloria,
vivrem beati d'eterno amore.

Hear me, Aida.
The land of Ethiopia
has once again awakened
to the fierce cry of a new war.
Your people have already invaded our land.
I shall command the Egyptian armies.
Amidst the noise
and cries of victory,
I shall prostrate myself before the King,
and reveal my heart to him.
You will be my crowning glory,
we will live blessed by eternal love.

AIDA

Nè d'Amneris paventi
il vindice furor? La sua vendetta,
come folgor tremenda,
cadrà su me, sul padre mio, su tutti.

And do you not fear Amneris'
vindictive anger?
Like some dreadful thunderbolt, her vengeance
will fall on me, on my father, and on us all.

RADAMES

Io vi difendo.

I will protect you.

AIDA

Invan! tu nol potresti.
Pur . . . se tu m'ami . . . ancor s'apre
una via di scampo a noi.

In vain! You will be powerless!
But . . . if you love me . . . there is
one way of escape for us.

RADAMES

Quale?

What is that?

AIDA

Fuggir.

Flight.

RADAMES

Fuggire!

Flight!

AIDA

Fuggiam gli ardori inospiti
di queste lande ignude;
una novella patria

Let us flee from the heat
of this barren dessert;
a new country;

al nostro amor si schiude.
Là, tra foreste vergini,
di fiori profumate,
in estasi beate
la terra scorderem,
in estasi la terra scorderem.

will welcome our love.
There, in virgin forests,
perfumed with flowers,
in beautiful ecstasy
we shall forget the world,
in ecstasy we shall forget the world.

RADAMES

Sovra una terra estrania
teco fuggir dovrei!
Abbandonar la patria,
l'are de' nostri dei!
Il suol dov'io raccolsi
di gloria i primi allori,
il ciel de' nostri amori
come scordar potrem?

I should flee with you
to a strange country?
Abandon my native land,
and the altars of our gods?
How could we forget the land
where I gathered the first laurels
of glory, and the sky
that first witnessed our love?

AIDA

Là, tra foreste vergini, *ecc.*

There, in virgin forests, *etc.*

RADAMES

I ciel
de' nostri amori, *ecc.* . . .

The sky
that first witnessed our love, *etc.* . . .

AIDA

Sotto il mio ciel più libero
l'amor ne fia concesso;
ivi nel tempio istesso
gli stessi numi avrem,
ivi nel tempio istesso, *ecc.*

Beneath my sky we could
enjoy a freer love;
there, in the same temple
have the same gods,
there, in the same temple, *etc.*

RADAMES

Abbandonar la patria,
l'are de' nostri dei!
Il ciel de' nostri amori
come scordar potrem?

Abandon my native land,
and the altars of our gods?
How could we forget
the sky that witnessed our love?

AIDA

Fuggiam, fuggiam!

Let us flee!

RADAMES

Aida!

Aida!

AIDA

Tu non m'ami. Va!

You do not love me. Go!

RADAMES

Non t'amo!

Not love you!

AIDA

Va!

Go!

RADAMES

Mortal giammai nè dio arse d'amor
al par del mio possente.

Never did mortal nor god
burn with a love as great as mine.

AIDA

Va, va, t'attende all'ara Amneris.

Go, go. Amneris awaits you at the altar.

RADAMES

No! giammai!

No! Never!

AIDA

Giammai, dicesti?
Allor, piombi la scure
su me, sul padre mio.

Never, you said?
Then, let the axe fall
on me and on my father.

RADAMES

Ah no! Fuggiamo!
Sì: fuggiam da queste mura,
al deserto insiem fuggiamo;
qui sol regna la sventura,
là si schiude un ciel d'amor.
I deserti interminati
a noi talamo saranno,
su noi gli astri brilleranno
di più limpido fulgor.

Ah no! Let us flee!
Yes: let us flee from these walls,
let us flee, together to the desert;
here, nothing but misfortune reigns,
there a paradise of love awaits us.
The endless desert
will be our bridal bed,
and the stars will shine above us
with a brighter light.

AIDA

Nella terra avventurata
de' miei padri, il ciel ne attende;
ivi l'aura è imbalsamata,
ivi il suolo è aromi e fior.
Fresche valli e verdi prati
a noi talamo saranno,
su noi gli astri brilleranno
di più limpido fulgor.

Heaven awaits us
in my ancestors' blessed country;
the breeze is sweetly perfumed there,
the soil is fragrant with flowers there.
Cool valleys and green meadows
will be our bridal bed,
and the stars will shine above us
with a brighter light.

AIDA *and* RADAMES

Vieni meco, insiem fuggiamo
questa terra di dolor.
Vieni meco, t'amo, t'amo!
A noi duce fia l'amore.

Come with me, together let us flee
this land of sorrow.
Come with me, I love you, I love you!
Love will be our guide.

AIDA

Ma, dimmi: per qual via
eviterem le schiere
degli armati?

But tell me: on what road
shall we avoid the legions
of the army?

RADAMES

Il sentier scelto dai nostri
a piombar sul nemico fia deserto
fino a domani.

The path chosen by our armies
for their march upon the enemy
will be deserted until tomorrow.

AIDA

E quel sentier?

What path is that?

RADAMES

Le gole di Nàpata.

The Napata gorges.

AMONASRO

Di Nàpata le gole!
Ivi saranno i miei.

The Napata gorges!
There my men will be there.

RADAMES

O! chi ci ascolta!

Oh! Who is listening to us?

AMONASRO

D'Aida il padre e degli etiopi il re!

Aida's father and the King of Ethiopia!

RADAMES

Tu! Amonasro! tu! il re?
Numi! che dissi?

You! Amonasro! You! the King?
Gods, what did I say?

No, non è ver, non è ver, non è ver,
no, no, no, non è ver, no!
Sogno, delirio è questo . . .

No, it is not true,
no, no, no, it is not true!
It is a dream, a delirium . . .

AIDA

Ah no! ti calma, ascoltami . . .

Ah no! Calm yourself, listen to me . . .

AMONASRO

A te l'amore d'Aida

Your love for Aida . . .

AIDA

. . . all'amor mio t'affida.

. . . trust in my love.

AMONASRO

. . . un soglio innalzera.

. . . will raise you to a throne.

RADAMES

Io son disonorato!
Per te tradii la patria!

I am dishonored!
I have betrayed my country for you!

AIDA

Ti calma!

Be calm!

AMONASRO

No: tu non sei colpevole:
era voler del fato.

No: you are not guilty:
it was the will of fate.

RADAMES

Io son disonorato!

I am dishonored!

AIDA

Ah no! Ah no!

Ah no! Ah no!

AMONASRO

No!

No!

RADAMES

Per te tradii la patria!

I have betrayed my country for you!

AMONASRO

No: tu non sei,
non sei colpevole.

No: you are not,
you are not guilty.

AIDA

Ti calma!

Be calm!

AMONASRO

Vien: oltre il Nil ne attendono
i prodi a noi devoti,
la del tuo cor i voti
coronera l'amor.
Vieni, vieni, vieni!

Come: the warriors devoted to us
await us there beyond the Nile;
there your heart's desire
love will crown.
Come, come!

AMNERIS
(coming out of the temple, followed by RAMFIS*)*

Traditor!

Traitor!

AIDA

La mia rival!

My rival!

AMONASRO

(threatening AMNERIS with a dagger)

L'opra mia a trugger vieni! Muori!	You come to destroy my plan! Die!

RADAMES

(stepping between them)

Arresta, insano!	Stop, madman!

AMONASRO

O rabbia!	O fury!

RAMFIS

Guardie, ola!	Hey there, guards!

RADAMES

(to AIDA and AMONASRO)

Presto! fuggite!	Quickly! Flee!

AMONASRO

(dragging AIDA away)

Vieni, o figlia.	Come, my daughter.

RAMFIS

(to the guards)

L'inseguite!	Follow them!

RADAMES

(to RAMFIS)

Sacerdote, io resto a te.	Priest, I am your prisoner.

ACT IV
Scene 1: A Hall in the King's Palace

A door leads to the subterranean chamber of justice.

AMNERIS

L'abborrita rivale a me sfuggia. Dai sacerdoti Radamès attende dei traditor la pena . . . Traditor egli non è . . . Pur rivelo di guerra l'alto segreto . . . egli fuggir volea . . . con lei fuggire . . . Traditori tutti! A morte! a morte! O! che mai parlo? Io l'amo, io l'amo sempre . . . Disperato, insano è quest'amor che la mia vita strugge. O! s'ei potesse amarmi! Vorrei salvarlo . . . E come? Si tenti!	My hated rival has escaped. Radames awaits a traitor's sentence from the priests . . . He is no traitor . . . Yet he revealed the great secret of the war . . . he wanted to flee . . . to flee with her . . . Traitors, all of them! Death to them! Death! Oh, what am I saying? I love him, I will always love him . . . This love which is destroying my life is hopeless, insane. Oh, if he could love me! I would save him. But how? I'll try!

(summoning the guards)

Guardie: Radamès qui venga.	Guards . . . let Radames come forth.

(Radames *is led in.)*

Già i sacerdoti adunansi
arbitri del tuo fato;
pur dell'accusa orribile
scolparti ancor t'è dato;
ti scolpa, e la tua grazia
io pregherò dal trono,
e nunzia di perdono,
di vita, a te sarò.

The priests are already gathering
to judge your fate;
but you may yet save yourself from this
horrible accusation;
justify yourself, and I will
plead for you before the throne,
and be a messenger,
bringing pardon and life to you.

Radames

Di mie discolpe i giudici
mai non udran l'accento;
dinanzi ai numi, agl'uomini
nè vil, nè reo mi sento.
Profferse il labbro incauto
fatal segreto, è vero,
ma puro il mio pensiero,
e l'onor mio restò.

The judges will never hear
words of excuse from me;
I feel neither despicable nor guilty
before gods or men.
My careless lips uttered
the fatal secret, it is true,
but my intention
and my honor remained untainted.

Amneris

Salvati dunque e scolpati.

Then claim your innocence and save yourself.

Radames

No!

No!

Amneris

Tu morrai.

You will die.

Radames

La vita abborro;
d'ogni gaudio la fonte inaridita,
svanita ogni speranza,
sol bramo di morir.

I hate life;
the fountain of every joy has run dry;
every hope has vanished
I want only to die.

Amneris

Morire!
Ah! tu dêi vivere!
Si, all'amor mio vivrai;
per te le angoscie orribili
di morte io già provai;
t'amai . . . soffersi tanto . . .
vegliai le notti in pianto . . .
e patria, e trono, e vita
tutto darei, tutto, tutto, darei per te.

To die!
Ah, you must live!
Yes, you shall live for my love;
I have already endured
the terrible anguish of death.
I loved you . . . I suffered so much . . .
I lay awake at night in tears . . .
and country, throne and life,
everything, everything I would give up for you.

Radames

Per essa anch'io la patria
e l'onor mio tradia.

I, too, betrayed my country
and my honor for her.

Amneris

Di lei non più!

No more of her!

Radames

L'infamia m'attende
e vuoi ch'io viva?
Miserio appien mi festi,
Aida a me togliesti,
spenta l'hai forse,
e in dono offri la vita a me?

Dishonor awaits me
and you want me to live?
You have filled me with wretchedness,
you have taken Aida from me,
perhaps you have killed her,
and as a gift you offer me life?

	AMNERIS
Io, di sua morte origine! No! vive Aida.	I, the cause of her death? No! Aida lives.
	RADAMES
Vive!	She lives!
	AMNERIS
Nei disperati aneliti dell'orde fuggitive sol cadde il padre.	Only her father fell in the desperate flight of fleeing hordes.
	RADAMES
Ed ella?	And she?
	AMNERIS
Sparve, nè più novella s'ebbe.	She disappeared and there has been no more news of her.
	RADAMES
Gli dei l'adducano salva alle patrie mura, e ignori la sventura di chi per le morrà!	May the gods lead her safely to her country's borders, and may she never know the fate of him who is about to die for her!
	AMNERIS
Ma, s'io ti salvo, giurami che più non la vedrai.	But, if I save you, swear to see her no more.
	RADAMES
Nol posso!	I cannot!
	AMNERIS
A le rinunzia per sempre e tu vivrai!	Renounce her forever and you shall live!
	RADAMES
Nol posso!	I cannot!
	AMNERIS
Anco una volta: a lei rinunzia.	Once again: renounce her.
	RADAMES
È vano.	It is useless.
	AMNERIS
Morir vuoi dunque, insano?	Do you wish to die, then, madman?
	RADAMES
Pronto a morir son gia.	I am prepared to die now.
	AMNERIS
Chi ti salva, sciagurato, dalla sorte che t'aspetta? In furore hai tu cangiato un amor ch'egual non ha. De' miei pianti la vendetta or dal ciel si compirà.	Who will save you, wretched man, from the fate that awaits you? You have changed a matchless love to hate. Now my tears will be avenged by heaven.
	RADAMES
È la morte un ben supremo se per lei morir m'è dato . . .	Death is a supreme joy if I may die for her.

AMNERIS

Ah! chi ti salva?

Ah, who will save you?

RADAMES

. . . nel subir l'estremo fato
gaudii immensi il cor avrà . . .

. . . my heart will know unsurpassed joy
in suffering the extreme penalty . . .

AMNERIS

De' miei pianti la vendetta
or dal ciel si compirà, *ecc.*

Now my tears will be avenged
by heaven, *etc.*

RADAMES

. . . gaudii immensi il cor avra,
l'ira umana più non temo,
temo sol la tua pietà.
L'ira umana, *ecc.*

. . . my heart will know unsurpassed joy,
I no longer fear human wrath,
I only fear your pity.
I no longer, *etc.*

(RADAMES *is led away by his guards.)*

AMNERIS

Ohimè! morir mi sento.
O! chi lo salva?
E in poter di costoro
io stessa lo gettai!
Ora, a te impreco,
atroce gelosia, che la sua morte
e il lutto eterno
del mio cor segnasti!

Alas! I shall surely die.
Oh, who will save him?
And I delivered him
into their power!
Now, I curse you,
vile jealousy, that pointed
the way to his death
and my heart's eternal grief!

(PRIESTS *cross the hall and enter the subterranean judgment chamber.)*

Ecco i fatali,
gl'inesorati ministri di morte.
O! ch'io non vegga
quelle bianche larve!
E in poter di costoro, *ecc.*

Here are the fatal
and inexorable ministers of death.
Oh, that I might not see
those white phantoms!
And I delivered him, *etc.*

RAMFIS *and* PRIESTS

(from the subterranean judgment chamber)

Spirto del nume.
sovra noi discendi!
Ne avviva al raggio
dell'eterna luce;
pel labbro nostro
tua giustizia apprendi.

Spirit of the god
descend upon us!
Strengthen us in the beams
of the eternal light;
through our lips
make thy justice known.

AMNERIS

Numi, pietà del mio straziato core.
Egli è innocente, lo salvate, o numi!
Disperato, tremendo è il mio dolore!

Gods, have pity on my anguished heart.
He is innocent, save him, O gods!
Desperate and boundless is my grief!

(RADAMES *is taken by his guards to the subterranean judgement chamber).*

RAMFIS *and* PRIESTS

Spirto del nume . . .

Spirit of the god . . .

AMNERIS

O! chi lo salva?

Oh, who will save him?

RAMFIS *and* PRIESTS

. . . sovra no discendi!

. . . descend upon us!

AMNERIS

O! chi lo salva? Mi sento morir!
Ohimè! ohimè! mi sento morir!

Oh, who will save him? I shall surely die!
Ah me! Ah me! I shall surely die!

RAMFIS

Radamès! Radamès! Radamès!
Tu rivelasti della patria i segreti
allo straniero.
Discolpati!

Radames! Radames! Radames!
You revealed your country's secrets
to the enemy.
Redeem yourself!

PRIESTS

Discolpati!

Redeem yourself!

RAMFIS

Egli tace.

He is silent.

RAMFIS *and* PRIESTS

Traditor!

Traitor!

AMNERIS

Ah, pietà! egli è innocente,
numi, pietà, numi, pietà!

Oh, mercy! He is innocent,
gods have pity, have pity!

RAMFIS

Radamès! Radamès! Radamès!
Tu disertasti dal campo
il dì che precedea la pugna.
Discolpati!

Radames! Radames! Radames!
You deserted your camp
the day preceding the battle.
Redeem yourself!

RAMFIS

Egli tace.

He is silent.

RAMFIS *and* PRIESTS

Traditor!

Traitor!

AMNERIS

Ah, pietà! ah! lo salvate,
numi, pietà, numi, pietà!

Ah, pity! Oh, save him,
O gods, have pity, have pity!

RAMFIS

Radamès! Radamès! Radamès!
Tua fè violasti,
alla patria spergiuro,
al re, all'onor.
Discolpati!

Radames! Radames! Radames!
You violated your trust
and betrayed your country,
king and honor.
Redeem yourself!

PRIESTS

Discolpati!

Redeem yourself!

RAMFIS

Egli tace.

He is silent.

RAMFIS *and* PRIESTS

Traditor!

Traitor!

AMNERIS

Ah, pietà! ah! lo salvate,
numi, pietà, numi, pietà!

Ah, pity! Oh, save him,
O gods, have pity, have pity!

RAMFIS *and* PRIESTS

Radamès, è deciso il tuo fato;

Radames, your fate is decided;

degli infami la morte tu avrai; sotto l'ara del nume sdegnato a te vivo fia schiuso l'avel.	you shall die a criminal's death; beneath the altar of the angry god you will find a living tomb.

AMNERIS

A lui vivo la tomba . . . o! gl'infami! nè di sangue son paghi giammai, e si chiaman ministri del ciel!	Alive in the tomb . . . Oh, the criminals! They are ever stained with blood, and they call themselves ministers of heaven!

RAMFIS *and* PRIESTS

(returning from the judgement chamber)

Traditor! Traditor! Traditor!	Traitor! Traitor! Traitor!

AMNERIS

Sacerdoti: compiste un delitto! Tigri infami di sangue assetate, voi la terra ed i numi oltraggiate, voi punite chi colpe non ha.	Oh priests, you have committed a crime! Wicked tigers, thirsting for blood, you have outraged heaven and earth, you have punished where there is no guilt.

RAMFIS

È traditor!	He is a traitor!

PRIESTS

È traditor!	He is a traitor!

RAMFIS *and* PRIESTS

Morrà!	He will die!

AMNERIS

(to RAMFIS*)*

Sacerdote: quest'uomo che uccidi, tu lo sai da me un giorno fu amato. L'antema d'un core straziato col suo sangue su te ricadra.	O prist, know that this man whom now you sentence was once loved by me. Along with his blood, the curses of a broken heart will fall upon your head!

RAMFIS

È traditor!	He is a traitor!

PRIESTS

È traditor!	He is a traitor!

RAMFIS *and* PRIESTS

Morrà!	He will die!

AMNERIS

Voi la terra ed i numi oltraggiate . . .	You have outraged both earth and heaven . . .

RAMFIS *and* PRIESTS

Morrà!	He will die!

AMNERIS

. . . voi punite chi colpe non ha. Ah no, non è traditor, *ecc.* Pietà! pietà! pietà! pietà!	. . . you have punished where there is no guilt. Ah no, he is no traitor, *etc.* Have mercy! Have mercy!

RAMFIS *and* PRIESTS

È traditor! morrà! *ecc.*
Traditor! Traditor! Traditor!

He is a traitor! He shall die! *etc.*
Traitor! Traitor! Traitor!

(RAMFIS *and the* PRIESTS *go out.)*

AMNERIS

Empia razza! anatema su voi!
La vendetta del ciel scenderà!
Anatema su voi!

Impious breed! a curse upon you!
Vengeance will descend from heaven!
A curse upon you!

Scene 2: The Interior of the Temple of Vulcan

The stage is divided into two floors: above, the temple; beneath, the crypt. Two priests are moving the stone which seals the entrance.

RADAMES

La fatal pietra sovra me si chiuse . . .
Ecco la tomba mia.
Del dì la luce
più non vedrò.
Non rivedrò più Aida.
Aida, ove sei tu? Possa tu almeno
viver felice e la mia sorte orrenda
sempre ignorar! Qual gemito!
Una larva . . . una vision . . .
No! forma umana è questa . . .
Ciel! Aida!

The fatal stone has closed over me . . .
Here is my tomb.
I will never see
the light of day again.
I will never again see Aida.
Aida, where are you? May you at least
live happily and never know
my unhappy fate! What cry is that?
A ghost . . . a vision . . .
No! It is a human form . . .
Heavens! Aida!

AIDA

Son io.

It is I.

RADAMES

Tu, in questa tomba!

You, in this tomb!

AIDA

Presago il core
della tua condanna,
in questa tomba
che per te s'apriva
io penetrai furtiva,
e qui lontana
da ogni umano sguardo,
nelle tue braccia desiai morire.

My heart warned me
of your condemnation;
into this tomb
which was being opened for you
I secretly made my way,
and here, far
from every human eye,
I wanted to die in your arms.

RADAMES

Morir! si pura el bella!
morir per me d'amore;
degli anni tuoi nel fiore
fuggir la vita!
T'avea il cielo per l'amor creata,
ed io t'uccido per averti amata!
No, non morrai!
troppo t'amai!
troppo sei bella!

To die! So pure and lovely!
To die for love of me;
to flee from life
in the flower of your youth!
Heaven created you for love,
and I am killing you by loving you!
No, you shall not die!
I have loved you too much!
You are too beautiful!

AIDA

(ecstatically)

Vedi? di morte l'angelo
radiante a noi s'appressa,
ne adduce a eterni gaudii
sovra i suoi vanni d'or.
Già veggo il ciel dischiudersi . . .
ivi ogni affanno cessa . . .
ivi comincia l'estasi
d'un immortale amor.

Do you see? The radiant angel of
death hastens toward us,
and carries us to eternal joy
upon his golden wings.
I already see heaven opening . . .
there, all sorrow ceases . . .
there, begins the ecstasy
of an immortal love.

PRIESTESSES

(in the temple above)

Immenso, immenso Fthà . . .

O mighty Ptah . . .

PRIESTS

Ah! . . .

Ah! . . .

AIDA

Triste canto!

Mournful chant!

RADAMES

Il tripudio dei sacerdoti.

The priests' song of rejoicing . . .

PRIESTESSES

. . . del mondo . . .

. . . spirit that . . .

PRIESTS

Ah! . . .

Ah! . . .

AIDA

Il nostro inno di morte.

Our hymn of death.

PRIESTESSES

. . . spirito animator . . .

. . . animates the world . . .

PRIESTS

Ah! . . .

Ah! . . .

RADAMES

(trying to move the stone which seals the crypt)

Nè le mie forti braccia smuovere ti
potranno, o fatal pietra!

Oh fatal stone,
even my strong arms cannot move you!

PRIESTS *and* PRIESTESSES

. . . noi t'invochiamo . . .

. . . we invoke thee . . .

AIDA

Invan!
Tutto è finito sulla terra per noi!

In vain!
All is finished for us on earth.

PRIESTS *and* PRIESTESSES

. . . t'invochiam . . .
. . . t'invochiam . . .

. . . we invoke thee . . .
. . . we invoke thee . . .

RADAMES

È vero! È vero!

It is true! It is true!

AIDA

O terra, addio;
addio, valle di pianti,
sogno di gaudio
che in dolor svani.
A noi si schiude il ciel
e l'alme erranti
volano al raggio dell'eterno di.

Farewell, O earth;
farewell, vale of tears,
dream of joy
that faded in sorrow.
Heaven opens for us
and our wandering souls
fly to the light of eternal day.

RADAMES

O terra, addio;
addio, valle di pianti . . .

Farewell, O earth;
farewell, vale of tears . . .

AIDA

O terra, addio.

Farewell, O earth.

RADAMES

. . . sogno di gaudio che in dolor svani.

. . . dream of joy which in sorrow faded.

AIDA

A noi si schiude . . .

For us open . . .

RADAMES

A noi si schiude il ciel . . .

The gates of heaven open to us . . .

AIDA

. . . si schiude il ciel . . .

. . . the gates of heaven . . .

RADAMES

. . . si schiude il ciel
e l'alme erranti . . .

. . . heaven opens
and our lost souls . . .

AIDA

. . . si schiude il ciel . . .

. . . heaven opens . . .

RADAMES

. . . volano al raggio
dell'eterno di.

. . . fly to the light
of eternal day.

AIDA

. . . a noi si schiude il ciel!

. . . heaven opens to us!

PRIESTS *and* PRIESTESSES

Immenso Fthà, noi t'invochiam . . .

Mighty Ptah, we call upon thee . . .

AIDA *and* RADAMES

Ah! si schiude il ciel!

Ah! heaven is opening to us!

PRIESTS *and* PRIESTESSES

. . . t'invochiam, t'invochiam!

. . . we call upon thee, we call upon thee!

(AMNERIS appears dressed in mourning and throws herself down upon the stone which seals the crypt.)

AIDA *and* RADAMES

O terra, addio;
addio, valle di pianti . . .

Farewell, O earth;
farewell, vale of tears . . .

AMNERIS

Pace t'imploro . . .

Peace I beg . . .

AIDA *and* RADAMES

. . . sogno di gaudio che in dolor svanì.

. . . dream of joy which in sorrow faded.

AMNERIS

. . . salma adorata . . .

beloved remains . . .

AIDA *and* RADAMES

A noi si schiude il ciel . . .

For us heaven opens . . .

AMNERIS

. . . Isi placata . . .

. . . may Isis, appeased . . .

AIDA *and* RADAMES

. . . si schiude il ciel
e l'alme erranti
volano al raggio dell'eterno dì.

. . . heaven opens
and our wandering souls
fly to the light of eternal day.

AMNERIS

. . . Isi placata ti schiuda il ciel!

. . . Isis, appeased, open heaven to you!

PRIESTS *and* PRIESTESSES

Noi t'invochiam . . .

We call upon thee . . .

AIDA

Il ciel . . .

Heaven . . .

RADAMES

Il ciel . . .

Heaven . . .

PRIESTS *and* PRIESTESSES

. . . noi t'invochiam . . .

. . . we invoke thee . . .

AIDA

. . . il ciel . . .

. . . heaven . . .

RADAMES

. . . il ciel . . .

. . . heaven . . .

PRIESTS *and* PRIESTESSES

. . . immenso Fthà . . .

. . . mighty Ptah . . .

AIDA *and* RADAMES

. . . si schiude il ciel, si schiude il ciel!

. . . heaven opens to us, heaven opens!

PRIESTS *and* PRIESTESSES

. . . immenso Fthà!

. . . mighty Ptah!

AMNERIS

Pace t'imploro, pace t'imploro,
pace, pace . . .
. . . pace!

Peace I beg, peace,
peace, peace . . .
. . . peace!

PRIESTS *and* PRIESTESSES

Immenso Fthà!

Mighty Ptah!

The Best Known Melodies from Aida

Act I, Scene 1

Celeste Aida

Sung by Radames

So! del Nilo al sacro lido

Sung by the King, Ramphis and Chorus

Act II, Scene 1

Amore, amore!

Sung by Aida

Allegro animato
A-mo - re, a - mo - re! gau-dio tor - men-to so - a-ve eb-
brez - za, an - sia cru-del

Act II, Scene 2

Gloria all' Eigtto ad Iside

Sung by the Chorus

Allegro maestoso
ff
Gloria all' E-git - to ad I - si-de che il sa-cro suol pro -
teg - ge! Al Re - che il Del - ta reg - ge, al
Re che il Del - ta reg - ge in-ni fe-sto - si al - ziam!

Triumphal March

Ma tu, Re

Sung by Amonasro and Aida

Poco piu animato
Ma tu, Re, tu si - gno - re pos - sen - te, a co -
sto - ro ti vol - gi cle - men - te Og - gi noi siam per - cos - si dal
fa - to, oh! do - man voi po - tria il fa - to col - pir.

Act III

Rivefrai le foreste

Sung by Amonasro and Aida

La tra foreste vergini

Sung by Aida

Si: fugiam da queste mura

Sung by Radames and Aida

Act IV, Scene 2

O terra addio

Sung by Radames and Aida

Glossary

Arcato. Played with a bow; bowed.

Aria. Elaborate composition for solo voice (occasionally a duet) with instrumental accompaniment. In contrast to songs, arias are characterized by highly formal vocal parts of some complexity, often displaying a singer's virtuosity.

Baritone. Male voice ranging between the bass and tenor, often combining the weight of the former with the lyrical flexibility of the latter.

Bass. The deepest of male voices.

Cabaletta. Originally *cavatinetta*. Short operatic song in popular style. Verdi used the term for the final sections of arias and duets written in faster tempos with uniform rhythms.

Chorus. A group of singers who perform concerted vocal or choral numbers in concerts, oratorios or operas. Opera choruses may number 300 or more voices and since the time of Gluck have been allowed to act. Also, the compositions written for such a group.

Coda. A concluding passage or section, beyond the basic structure of a composition, added to obtain or to heighten the sense of finality.

Contrapuntal. Term used in connection with the art of blending melodies according to the laws of counterpoint.

Duet. A vocal or instrumental composition written in two parts or for two performers.

Ensemble. A group of performers whose simultaneous presentation of complementary parts contributes to a single effect.

Finale. The last scene of an operatic act, when on an extended scale, written in several movements or sections, often involving some quick dramatic action.

Grand Opera. In the strict sense, French opera in which every word is sung and all recitative passages are accompanied by the orchestra. The term is more loosely used to describe serious opera in all forms.

Harmonics. High-pitched tones of flutelike quality produced on a stringed instrument by lightly touching the string instead of pressing it against the fingerboard.

Intermezzo. Originally, an entertainment introduced between the acts of a serious drama, later with comedy and opera as well, serving to provide time for scenery changes, to permit the performers to rest and to briefly divert the audience's attention, relieving the strain of the more demanding performance. The intermezzo was later replaced by the use of ballet material and the entr'acte, a musical interlude generally relating closely to the action on stage.

Legato. Term used to indicate music performed without any apparent break between the notes.

Libretto. The text for a dramatic vocal work, such as an opera, oratorio, etc.

Lyric, lyrical. Used to describe the qualities of music, the term indicates material of a poetic nature, subjective, sensual, as compared to work of dramatic or narrative content. The opposition of lyric and dramatic material is often the source of basic contrast in music.

Melodic Interval. An interval is the distance in pitch from one tone to another on a given scale. When sounded succesively, it is a melodic interval.

Mezzosoprano. Female voice ranging between the soprano and contralto.

Motif. From *leitmotif*, a term used to indicate a theme of readily recognizable melodic, har monic or rhythmic form. First used in connection with a specific character or incident, such a theme returns time and again, reminiscent of the original association.

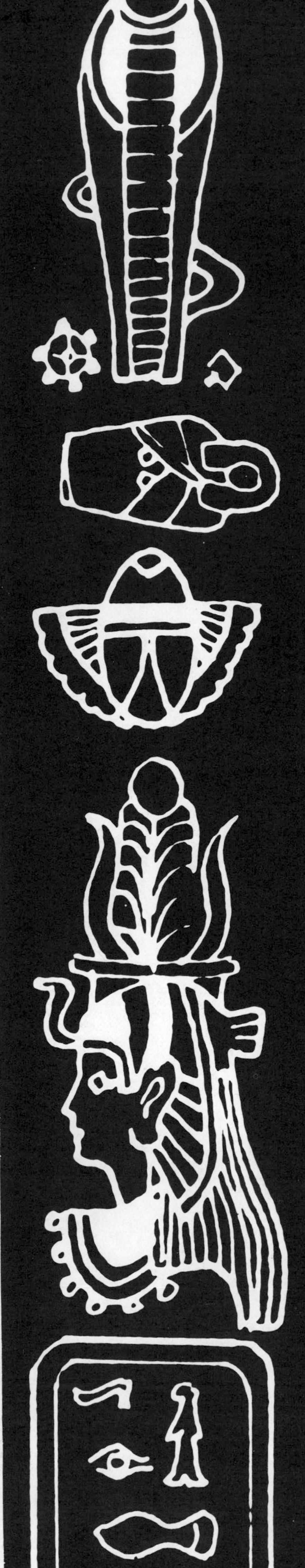

Orchestral Coloring. When applied to orchestration, frequently thought of in terms of "color", the expression may describe the various intensities in the overtones of musical sounds, producing different timbres (the quality of tone that distinguishes one instrument from all others), or to describe details of performance and interpretation.

Overture. Instrumental music composed to introduce a larger composition, usually an opera, though often a symphony or suite.

Pizzicato. "Plucked" or "pinched". An indication that the strings of a member of the violin family are to be plucked with the finger instead of bowed.

Prelude. Term applied to introductory music used for an operatic overture that does not follow a strict form, emphasizing that the music is related to what follows.

Recitative. Vocal style designed for the declamation of narrative episodes in an opera or oratorio in the rhythm of natural speech with slight melodic variation. Also, a passage rendered in this form.

Scene. When applied to opera, the term indicates a movement, usually for the solo voice, distinguished from the recitative and aria by its dramatic quality and length.

Soprano. Female voice of high range and bright quality; classified as dramatic, lyric and coloratura.

Tenor. Highest natural adult male voice.

Tremolo, tremolando. Term applied to the rapid reiteration of a single note or chord without regard to measured time values. An important effect on all stringed instruments, it is often used for dramatic moments or as a background for melodies played by other instruments. Term also applies to the rapid alternation of two notes, produced by a quick motion of the finger, not the bow.

Trio. Designation for a group of three performers; also the music they perform.

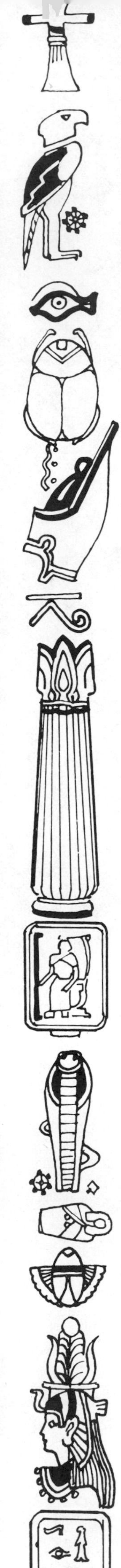

A Chronological Listing of Verdi's Operas

	First Performance Date; Theater; City	*Librettist*
Oberto, Conte Di Bonifacio	Nov. 17, 1839 La Scala, Milan	Piazza, Merelli, Solera
Il Finto Stanislao (Un Giorno Di Regno)	Sept. 5, 1840 La Scala, Milan	Romani
Nabucodonosor	Mar. 9, 1842 La Scala, Milan	Solera
I Lombardi Alla Prima Crociata	Feb. 11, 1843 La Scala, Milan	Solera
["I Lombardi" revised as "Jerusalem"; new numbers and ballet added]	Nov. 26, 1847 Opera, Paris	Royer, Vaez
Ernani *Fenice, Venice*	Mar. 9, 1844 Piave	
I Due Foscari	Nov. 3, 1844 Argentina, Rome	Piave
Giovanna D'Arco	Feb. 15, 1845 La Scala, Milan	Solera
Alzira	Aug. 12, 1845 S. Carlo, Naples	Cammarano
Attila	Mar. 17, 1846 Fenice, Venice	Solera
Macbeth	Mar. 14, 1847 Pergola, Florence	Piave, Maffei
["Macbeth" revised; changed orchestration, added new numbers and ballet].	Apr. 21, 1865 Lyrique, Paris	Nuitter, Beaumont
I Masnadieri	July 22, 1847 Her Majesty's, London	Maffei
Il Corsaro	Oct. 25, 1848 Grande, Trieste	Piave
La Battaglia Di Legnano	Jan. 27, 1849 Argentina, Rome	Cammarano
Luisa Miller	Dec. 8, 1849 S. Carlo, Naples	Cammarano
Stiffelio	Nov. 16, 1850 Grande, Trieste	Piave

["Stiffelio" revised as "Aroldo"; new last act]	Aug. 16, 1857 Nuovo, Rimini	Piave
Rigoletto	Mar. 11, 1851 Fenice, Venice	Piave
Il Trovatore	Jan. 19, 1853 Apollo, Rome	Cammarano Bardare
La Traviata	Mar. 6, 1853 Fenice, Venice	Piave
2nd Production	May 6, 1854 S. Benedetto, Venice	
I Vespri Siciliani	June 13, 1855 Opera, Paris	Scribe, Duveyrier
Simone Boccanegra	Mar. 12, 1857 Fenice, Venice	Piave
["Simone Boccanegra" re-orchestrated; text revised and scenes added]	Mar. 24, 1881 La Scala, Milan	Boito
Un Ballo In Maschera	Feb. 17, 1859 Apollo, Rome	Somma
La Forza Del Destino	Nov. 10, 1862 Imperial, St. Petersburg	Piave
["La Forza Del Destino" revised; numbers added; sequence of scenes and text last act changed; prelude replaced by overture]	Feb. 27, 1869 La Scala, Milan	Ghislanzoni
Don Carlo	Mar. 11, 1867 Opera, Paris	Mery, du Locle
["Don Carlo" revised; reduced from five acts to four]	Jan. 10, 1884 La Scala, Milan	
Aida	Dec. 24, 1871 Opera, Cairo	Ghislanzoni
2nd Production	Feb. 8, 1872 La Scala, Milan	
Otello	Feb. 5, 1887 La Scala, Milan	Boito
Falstaff	Feb. 9, 1893 La Scala, Milan	Boito

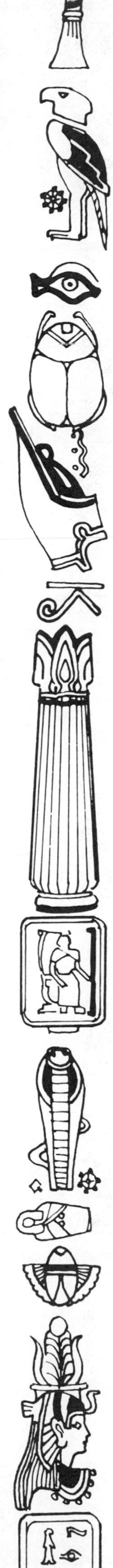

AIDA

OPERA IN 4 ATTI E 7 QUADRI

PAROLE DI A. GHISLANZONI

MUSICA DEL COMM[RE] G. VERDI

SCRITTA PER COMMISSIONE

DI SUA ALTEZZA IL KEDIVE

PER IL TEATRO DELL' OPERA

DEL CAIRO

E RAPPRESENTATA PER LA PRIMA VOLTA

SU QUESTE SCENE

Nel mese di Decembre 1871.

CAIRO

TIPOGRAFIA FRANCESE DELBOS-DEMOURET

1871

First page of the program, translated into Arabic.

ترجمة

الاوبيره المسماة باسم

عايدة

تاليف المعلم غيزلنسونى وتوقيع الاوستة ويردى

مصنفه

بامر سعادة خديو مصر

تعريب

العبد الفقير ابى السعود افندى

محرر صحيفة وادى النيل

(الطبعة الاولى)

بمطبعة جرنال وادى النيل بالقاهره

سنة ١٢٨٨

First page of the program for the first production of Aida.

A photograph of Verdi and his family in the 1890s.

The Bettmann Archive

Verdi leaving his coach surrounded by admirers.

The Bettmann Archive